MEMORY BAY

MEMORY BAY

by

John Frederic Gibson

1724

LONGMANS, GREEN AND CO
LONDON ⟡ NEW YORK ⟡ TORONTO

LONGMANS, GREEN AND CO LTD
6 & 7 CLIFFORD STREET LONDON W I

ALSO AT MELBOURNE AND CAPE TOWN

LONGMANS, GREEN AND CO INC
55 FIFTH AVENUE NEW YORK 3

LONGMANS, GREEN AND CO
215 VICTORIA STREET TORONTO I

ORIENT LONGMANS LTD
BOMBAY CALCUTTA MADRAS

First published in 1950

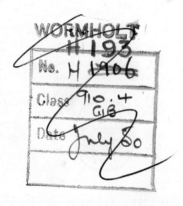
PRINTED IN GREAT BRITAIN
BY WESTERN PRINTING SERVICES LTD, BRISTOL

CONTENTS

HAMMERSMITH

NOTE

Acknowledgments are made to the Editor of
the *Cornish Review* for permission to reprint
parts of Chapter One which originally appeared
in that journal.

THE LIZARD LIGHT

OUTSIDE my window, a young moon shines over the sea; the tide is low, and the wind has died away. If I look out towards the horizon I can see the mast lights of ships, some setting out for distant oceans, some returning from long wanderings. Those lights flicker under the clouds and move slowly to be hidden by the dark cliff faces. If I followed my eyes, and went out over the water, I would cross the curvature of the earth, not touching land until I came to the green shores near the mouth of the Amazon. So the winds that drift in to our little cove might bring the scents of hot jungles, the dust of torrid zones, the wet mists of the Atlantic, or the scents of Spanish orange groves. But the sea is wide, and the outer world is but a memory. It is wise, therefore, to turn inland and look towards the dark face of the Cornish heath.

Directly opposite, the lights of the village shine out, golden squares in the blue moonlight. The cottages rise up in tiers above the fishing beach. The boats can just be seen, silent and deserted; they lie clear of the high-water mark. A cigarette glimmers nearby as one of the fishermen prepares his gear for the dawn launching. Above and behind the village, the heath stretches away to the little grey town that stands squarely and firmly, guarding the approaches to our promontory.

This land of Cornwall is of many colours. When the sun is out, and the stunted palms are bright against a blue sky, and the cottages gleam white, and the pine branches cast dark shadows, then it is all warmth and brilliance. The orange fungus on the rocks is vivid; the wild flowers dance above the grasses; the shallow water is as green as ice. But when the skies are grey, the colour is lost, and the place is bleak and cold, as barren as the rocks below Cape Wrath. No day is like another, and each morning look from the window reveals

I

a new mood, a fresh face on the land that we think we know so well.

To-night, the waters of the cove are resting; small waves whisper among the rocks, and the air is never without the murmur of the tide, but the storm has passed and the rain is sweeping towards the east.

From these cliffs, I first saw dawn over the sea. The lighthouse on Lizard Head paled. The horizon became a dark line under a green sky. Twin lights, far out on the water, became a homeward-bound tanker. The surf was like silver lace. Far to the east, a few broken and twisted trees were black against the sunrise.

I was standing about a hundred and twenty feet above the water, shivering a little because the dawn air was cold. The sea heaved sluggishly against the rocks. Turning, I could see the little cottage that lay by itself among the gorse and sloe bushes. A light burned in my window. It had been dark when I left and I had forgotten the switch in my hurry to reach the cliff edge by daybreak. I had left a small room, my bed, my shelf of books with volumes of Stevenson, Jack London, Melville; I had run, eyes wide with look-ing, down to the point where the coastguards had a tall, white flagpole.

After an hour's tense waiting, I saw what had drawn me out on that clear morning. She came from behind Lizard Head, her sails shining pink, her long white hull sliding through the green and grey waves. Beyond her, the horizon was turning blue, and I thought of the great waters through which she had sailed and of the hot, strange, foreign ports that she had visited. All those far-off places were a great mystery to me. I had read of them, but the sight of the four-masted barque gently creeping into the lee of England made me conscious of the firmness of the granite rocks under my feet. That ship met the glitter of sunrise; she was something out of a dream, and, when she had vanished behind Black Head, the sea was empty except for an old coaster that plunged along, smoke swirling in her wake. The enchantment faded. I turned away, going back to the small room where my books seemed to mock. I leaned into the sunlight, staring at the breadth of the sea. And then I heard a whisper on the wind. It may have been the tide creasing in the bay, or the long summer grasses bending in the fields; it may have been the pine needles stroking the grey tiles of the roof. But it seemed to speak, to tell me that the sea was there for all men to know, and that I could sail its far reaches, as did the men on the ships that passed over the horizon and were lost to view.

Since that morning, I have learned something of the seas and oceans of the world, their length, breadth, and even their depth. So, to-night, I look out over the placid waters, shining under the moon, and my mind goes out to the great waves of Cape Horn, or the hot, dead waters of the Gulf of Aden, or, perhaps, the dark and silent surface of a Norwegian fjord. Divided by great distances, these visions are all part of the same memory, for the sea, whatever face it presents, is but one body of water, and the smallest wave that dies against the shores of England is related to the crested giants that sweep over the South Pacific.

*   *   *

Cornwall was strange and exciting to a boy of twelve. The cottage in which we were staying was called Caerleon. It was at the world's end, for the road from London crossed into a new country when it ran over the Cornish border, and the Lizard, like most peninsulas, is detached from the rest of Cornwall. It is, as yet, without a railway, and its life is self-contained and remote. It idles in the quiet way of its inhabitants, those who till the earth and fish in the sea.

Passing through Helston, the road wound before us, leading to Ruan Minor, and there, far below, the sea stretched away to meet the white clouds. It seemed as if we had come to the end of our journey, but a narrow track led from the eastern end of the village, and we left the houses behind, running down between hedges of sloe and blackthorn and wild roses, and, at length, seeing the blue water on either side. There, under a single dark pine, the cottage

3

lay alone, whitewashed and clean, facing out over the wild ground that ran up to the headland.

That was the *mise en scène*. It was a solitary place, basking in sunlight from dawn to dusk, or swept by all the power of all the gales. There was a little garden in front, a green lawn, some rose beds, and the red and pink fuchsia around the borders. Banks of veronica lay against the white walls. The advantages of such a place were obvious. Down to the left of the headland, a small cove lay between the grass-covered cliffs. There could bathe and look for topaz and clamber on the rocks. Out of the water our clothes were scanty. In the water we discarded everything and swam unimpeded. The disadvantages were, I suppose, lumped together into a lack of social facilities. There were, in other words, no cinemas, no tennis courts, no billiard tables or amusement parks. So, for many, life would have been a dull thing indeed, but we did not suffer from boredom. If the water was cold, the cliffs were always open for climbing. If the gales blew, we could explore the cottage for an old smugglers' passage that was supposed to run down to the cove. When we grew tired of the cottage, we could walk around the cliff path to where the fishermen lived and to where the boats were propped upright on the shingle beach. Occasionally, we went out into the bay in a little white motor-boat and trolled for mackerel.

Those who live on the edges of the Cornish cliffs might as well be at sea. Their homes are shaken by the winds. The thatches quiver, and security is threatened. Spray drives against the windows. And then the sun comes out and the waters draw back their strength. The place sleeps. The tide rises and falls, and the cottages are becalmed under the incurious stars.

The village that lay a mile or two to the west of Caerleon Cottage was a village of the sea. Coming down the steep hill, one turned a corner and saw, between thatches, a triangle of blue water above a scarlet splash of geranium blossom. The green tamarisk branches fluttered in the breeze. The road swung right and passed across the beach before its long and tortuous climb up the opposite slope. Down by the fishing boats, nets dried in the sun, and lobster pots gleamed white where the willow was thick with salt. The place smelled of seaweed and tar and brine. The fishermen sat and stared towards the horizon.

That was the summer picture, one of ease and tranquillity. At other times, the waves came over the road, and the boats were put away into the dark, slate-roofed sheds, and the days were thankfully short. In the spring, when the cliffs were a riot of flowers and the violets were purple in the hedges, the blood began to flow again and the young rabbits sheltered under the stone walls, waiting for the summer. In the spring, easterly gales would come tearing down the Channel, smashing the waves against the rocks so that the air was full of spray and tiny rainbows. But the gales did not last for long, and, in no time, the boats were out and away, eager to be in action once more, proud of their shining coats of blue and green paint.

To go out to the lobster grounds in the first spring calm is rather like walking over the grasses of a freshly sown lawn. There is a sense of triumph. At last, after great preparation and long waiting, the hour is at hand. Spring is not just a thing of cuckoos and lambs and pretty blossoms; it means that the death-like hibernation can cease, and, most important, the nearly empty purses can be refilled.

We gather on the beach at dawn. In the half-darkness there are sharp sounds: the rattle of footsteps on the shingle; the striking of a match; the falling of a rowlock on to the bottom boards of a boat, virginal boards that are, as yet, free of fish scales. There are lights in some of the cottages and late arrivals are silhouetted in their open doorways as they look up at the sky before hurrying down to join us.

It is cold. The rocks are still holding the chill of winter, and the air stings the bottoms of our lungs. As I wait, a dark figure comes over and bangs a bucket of fresh bait into the boat. The new pots are already aboard, stacked in the stern. "Right," growls a voice, "off we go."

Hands come out of the darkness, and the boat rocks gently as it slides almost silently towards the water. Then, for the first time for months, the water laps against the keel, and the planking shines in the pallid light of daybreak. There is a moment of hesitation, and then we are waterborne and drifting out from the line of foam along the shore. The swell, a reminder of last week's gale, lifts us and drops us. The marine engine stutters into life, zombie-like after its winter's rest, a trifle stiff in the joints. Then there is nothing to do for a while but sit and listen to the *phut-phutting* of the engine and feel the heat of the rising sun slowly pass through our skin and warm our innermost bones. There is time to smoke, time to watch the gannets flying, time to settle comfortably against the transom and dream of the outer seas.

We reach the lobster ground of our choice, and the engine is throttled back as the pots go over the side. We see them sink into the blue water, swirling under, the rope that joins them snaking out over the gunwale. And that is all for the first day. The corks are left bobbing on the tide, and a little black flag waves jauntily. Fifty pots, with fresh bait inside them, lie on the bottom of the bay. Blue lobsters are down there too, and crabs, spider crabs, crayfish and such-like will be moving in the dark-green light. We imagine all this as we steer for home. If the weather holds, to-morrow will be the day for reaping that harvest of the sea. If a gale blows, the pots will be dragged from the rocks, hurled about in deep water, to be cast up on our beach, smashed and useless. The work of a winter will be undone.

We come gently to the shallow water and run our bows on to the beach. Now, the fishermen can wander up to their cottages in search of a late breakfast. For me, it is a question of walking back to Caerleon along the cliff path, and taking a short cut across the fields where the little black bullocks stand. As I pass, they turn and stare as if I am a strange monster from some other planet. They watch me until I am out of sight behind the tall hedges.

*   *   *

There were nine crabbers on the beach, two men to each boat. These crabbers were about twenty-five feet long, broad-beamed and strongly built. Sails and centre boards were a thing of the past, but the masts that were stepped in the stern, about two feet forward of the transom, were of some practical use. From them it was possible to set a triangular mizzen which kept the boat steady when hauling nets.

Unlike their boats, the fishermen were of varied sizes and shapes. I took passage in a steel-grey crabber belonging to Rambo Stevens, the largest man in the cove. His partner, known as Doctor Cook, was small and thin. Rambo was senior officer, but, unlike many overlords, he did most of the hard work, cutting the bait, baiting the pots, starting the engine and so on. Doctor Cook was at the tiller while we motored from one place to another, and, I believe, he was responsible for the boat's maintenance between one trip and the next.

As the tides flowed later each day, so the boats departed later, and when I went out to help haul the nets and lift the pots, we were not clear of the beach until well after sunrise.

It took us half an hour to cross the bay and come to the place where we had dropped the pots. Far down the coast, towards Mullion, other boats were coming out, their little triangular sails black on the shining water, the beat of their engines drawing the gulls out from the cliffs.

There was time to look around. The smoke from our pipes floated up in the sunlight. The cliffs were black and green, and above them the fields were very green indeed. The gorse was as brilliant as the fields of daffodils over by the village. The wooden gunwale grew warm under my arm.

There is an unfading excitement about hauling up the bottom nets. We found our little flag, leaning over, its cork float straining in the last of the tide. Rambo cut the engine, and the silence was sudden and immense. With practised skill, Doctor Cook leaned over the bows and hooked in the corks. We were anchored. There was a moment of peace while we tied on oilskin aprons, and then the real business began. Doctor Cook stayed in the bows. I took up position near the centre thwart, and Rambo growled away in the stern. We hauled on the cold, wet rope. The end of the net came inboard, crowding over the roller. My interest quickened. For a while there was nothing but net and seaweed, and then a skate slithered over the gunwale, blinking its gills at us, flapping its tail lazily in our faces. After that, six crayfish came in, one after the other, their yellow shells gleaming. By the time the end of the net arrived we had eleven crayfish and three skate. Rambo shook his head and grumbled. He started the engine and sailed merrily over to the first string of pots.

I found that hauling pots was the best part of the morning's work. True, there would be no strange monsters, no giant flatfish, but we could expect lobster, and the sight of the blue-green of a large-sized lobster made up for all the empty pots. I think Rambo preferred pots too. He used to prepare for the fray with great gusto, rubbing his hands and squinting up at the sky from under the peak of his old cap. Doctor Cook's feelings were undiscernible.

I used to lean over the side, watching the pots as they came up through the translucent water. First there would be a vague shadow, then a barred shape, and lastly the detailed outline with its stone weights. Sometimes there might be a lobster or a crab on the top of the pot and we would have to haul slowly and carefully. Young lobsters would advertise their presence by flapping all over the pot, but the older ones were quieter and dignified in defeat. Crabs always seemed to be stunned by their misfortune, and would move with a purposeless amble around the curve of the willows whence they could be easily picked and dropped on to the bottom boards. So it went on, pot after pot. The sun rose, and our sweaters were unnecessary. Rambo tossed the old bait, saturated and limp, to the awaiting gulls. The birds welcomed what the lobsters had refused.

Once we found a small white octopus rolling around with a red and useless spider crab. The crab went over the side, its legs waving crazily; the octopus clung to my hand in a frenzy of affection. We took it back to the cove and put it in a clear pool that had been left by the receding tide. It seemed happy enough there, and walked around with a gentle swaying of the hips. Next day it had gone.

From the garden of Caerleon, we could watch the boats moving back and forth in the sheen of the sunlight. They looked happy to be out there, but we were only onlookers, and I knew very well that the fishermen who looked up and saw us would be frowning with envy. Fishing was an amusement for us; for them it was work, and as such they hated it.

It was possible to go out on the blue waters of that bay a hundred times and still feel like an explorer. It all depended on the colour of the water, the type of fish to be caught or the simple fact that in one case everyone was there for pleasure, while in another the professionals were eager to be back home. Trolling for mackerel was always a sport. We used a white motor-boat that lacked the austerity touch of the others. It took us out beyond the rock that is known as Carrick Luz, and swung back, the wake curving delicately. Then the lines would be out, spinners flashing at the correct depth, for the month. The motor would be eased down, and after that it was up to the fish.

Summer trolling is a lazy, peaceful occupation, suitable for the siesta hour. The three or four fishers can become absorbed in their own thoughts, lulled into a dream by the sun's heat, the throbbing of the marine engine, and the glare of the water which makes closed eyes seem natural enough. Only the man at the tiller need watch out, and the waters are deep enough until one is in the actual shadow of the cliffs. So each man sits there, worlds apart from the next, one finger alive and alert, feeling the jerk of the line. Apart from those fingers, the bodies can be relaxed and minds can wander far and away. There is nothing there that is not immense. The sky is solid, hot and blue. The sea fades away into a haze. The land is a remote façade of black and green, dwindling to east and west. The boat is small, as are the gulls around, but the boat is forgotten as we dream. . . .

We strike a shoal, and the fish glitter and flash in the clear water. And our lines are taut and quivering. We wake abruptly, grinning with success as the fish come inboard, their striped bodies flapping, their scales lying like circles of mica on the bottom boards. Sometimes we find a garfish on the hooks. It is unexciting to catch, but there is a fascination in eating its white meat, for the backbone is as green as an emerald.

Sometimes there were over sixty fish in the boat as we turned to meet the shadows that were spreading out over the bay. The sun went quickly into the skyline as we ran our bows on to the beach, and then there was the quick business of hauling the boat clear of the tide. We would go up the road, taking the cliff path home, tired and sunburned, sleepy with the mellow heat of the evening.

Over Caerleon the pine was a black sentinel, motionless as we passed. The lonely cottage became a world of its own, all the distances of the universe shrinking to be within our little sphere, between the white walls and the veronica hedge. The golden lights that streamed from the windows did not reach far, and out in the darkness there was only a silent emptiness where nothing moved. Indoors, it was bright with welcome. From the window of my little bedroom I looked across the hidden heath. Far out, a star was rising over the horizon, and the wash of the summer waves on the rocks was a gentle whisper. It was a night of sudden, sharp noises, between which there was a breathless pause, the enchantment of unknown and secret movement. The lighthouse flicked out every three seconds, a regular beat that was thrown in gold reflection on the panes of the open window.

*   *   *

I used to think that old Captain Hugh, owner of Caerleon, was the luckiest man alive. To live in such a beautiful place, for every hour of every day, seemed to me incredibly wonderful. But, as he said, most of his life had been spent at sea, for he had rounded the Horn eleven times, and he told me stories of the old days in China and Australia. He knew of the stars, of distant ports and lands; he knew of the moods of the sea and of men.

"I should like to live here," I said. "All the time."

"And how would you earn your living?"

"I haven't thought of that yet."

Captain Hugh, who was picking fleas out of the Sealyham's back, shook his head. "A publisher lived here before me. Grant Richards. There were often writers here. Perhaps you could do that."

"Yes, perhaps."

"It won't be easy."

"How does one begin?"

"Go out, as I did, and see the world. See men and women in all countries, in all stages of civilisation. Forget about your aim for at least ten years and then begin to practise your art. You may need ten years at that."

I must have looked dismayed, for he added: "It is rather like a long voyage. For instance, I might have left San Francisco for Falmouth, via the Horn. Always I head for Falmouth, but the Lizard light will not be seen for many months. I look up at the stars, at Capella and Sirius. I see Magellan's Clouds, a bright cluster near the South Pole. Lights shine in my eyes but that does not dim my first sight of the Lizard. Pick yourself a star and remember it, but don't expect to see it clearly all the time."

I never doubted Captain Hugh's wisdom. He knew about all things. "You had the Lizard light," I said. "Which shall be my star?"

He smiled, and led me out into the quiet darkness.

"Do you know Cassiopeia?"

"No."

"The Great Bear?"

"Yes."

"The Pole Star?"

"Yes."

"Good. Well, draw a line from the Bear through the Pole Star and you'll come to Cassiopeia. Then just to the right is a bright little star. Just to the east. Can you see? There are two together."

After a while I found the two stars. Captain Hugh chuckled. "There you are. The Lizard light."

"But . . ."

"That's Lacerta, the Lizard. You and I can have the same guides. Keep your eye on it." He went indoors and left me alone under the night sky. Lacerta twinkled down at me; it seemed right overhead. To the west, the lighthouse flashed in the summer air. Beyond, the sea was a black shimmer of calm reflection. But I was looking up at my new friend. Lacerta. It was small and insignificant and terribly distant. But it was there to guide. One day, I would no longer need its light. One day I would live by the Cornish shore, every hour of every day, and the star would shine on, a reminder of voyages and meetings, happiness and sorrow. It would be always there, the star before youth, the lighthouse before the retired sailor. Whichever way one looked, there was a clear light.

CHAPTER TWO

NORTHERN LIGHTS

On a certain morning in the August of 1936, I was sitting on the trunk of a fallen tree beside a narrow river. In spite of the fact that I was roughly two hundred miles inside the Arctic Circle, the air was warm. The birches were a bright, gay green against the sky. Not far away were three wooden cabins, their walls weathered to a dark grey. These were the homes of the Lapps, for I was on holiday in the northern triangle of Finland, between Lake Enare and the Arctic Ocean.

Over to the west, where the river tumbled from the placid waters of a lake, the Lapps were busy preparing for the winter. I knew them all well, for our two tents were on the edge of the same lake and it was my job to wander down the river and catch our breakfast. As soon as the sun appeared over the hills of Russia, I would be up, taking the split cane trout rod down to the deep pools. The best place for trout or grayling was across the river, near the Lapp settlement. At first, I used to call across to the men on the opposite bank, and if their temper was good they would come over for me in one of their unstable boats. At the start, they were a little afraid. Perhaps they objected to our presence. Perhaps they were shy. But after a while they were always waiting with the boat, eager to be given a cigarette and to be allowed to wind the reel in and out.

Those mornings were delightful, each one a little different from the others. I can remember one that was almost perfect. I was woken earlier than usual, partly by the cold and partly by the stamping of the reindeer outside the tent. The air held the bite of winter as I slipped from my sleeping-bag; it remained as cold as steel until the pale sun was up over the tops of the pines. The clearing between the tents was shining with dew; the scene was near-white in the intangible light that covers the Arctic summers for twenty-four hours a day. The ashes of our night fire lay under a windless sky, each burnt twig retaining its shape. Between the crooked birch branches, the lake lay like a sheet of polished steel.

It was very still. The essential silence seemed to obscure sounds that I knew must exist. For instance, if I listened very carefully, I could hear the rippling of the river, and if I concentrated on the sight of a moving boat, I could hear the squeak of the oars against the gunwale. But the silence was the noticeable thing; it was like a curtain that slipped through the trees and enclosed me within itself.

The waters of the lake were abruptly broken as a flight of duck came down with a soft whistling, their bodies ploughing little waves. The moss under my feet was soft, yet it had a crispness from the night frost. The bilberry plants were motionless; not a leaf stirred.

Knowing that our fingers would be stiff and clumsy at dawn, it was our habit to make up the rods and casts before nightfall. So looking around I found the gear ready against a tree. I had only to lace my boots, collect pipe and matches and light the camp fire before setting off for the river.

Coming from the trees into the open, I saw that a boat had come for me. I waved, and in reply the Lapp raised his short pipe to the level of his forehead. His great dogs played around in the reeds, looking for a stick that had been thrown there; their barks broke across the stillness like rifle shots during a truce.

The man who had come for me on that particular day was the one we called Lenin; he grinned as he held out his hand for my rod. He was a large man, but squat and Mongolian. He had a smell of his very own, one of leather, tobacco, fish, wood smoke and the mosquito oil we had given him a few days before. It was a pleasant smell.

For all his size, Lenin was light-weight; he remained in the boat as I pushed her off the mud and jumped aboard. The sun peeped over the eastern trees, slashing the country with green. A small white cow wandered around, dazzling in the new light; she tinkled along, for her owners had hung a little bell around her neck. The sweet sound of this bell was somewhat misleading. More often than not it spelled danger. These little cows were among the worst-tempered of animals. They attacked swiftly and always from the rear.

Lenin was pleased with himself that morning; he jabbered away over his shoulder, indicating that he had shot a vast goose on the previous evening, and that his wife was in a better mood. As he talked, the blades of the oars swung in steady circles, in and out of the sunlight; the falling drops were like topaz; the water gurgled beneath the bow.

We progressed slowly on our way. The two dogs followed astern; they swam strongly, their bluff chests forcing out two miniature bow waves. Lenin whistled shrilly. The dogs took no notice, but the sound drew a group of silent, wide-eyed children from one of the cabins.

Not wishing to become involved in a family gathering, I jumped out as soon as the boat grounded and with a quick "thank you" went off down the stream to my pool. Mrs. Lenin would get her gossip and a fish or two when I returned. Until then, she would have to pass the time baking some of her rock-like bread or hacking up a strip of pemmican. Both these jobs would keep her busy and Lenin would be able to smoke a peaceful pipe without interruption. I whistled to the tame Siberian jay who flew behind me. He knew that I would clean the fish by the river bank and never failed to turn up.

The morning was vivid. As soon as I was round the corner, out of sight, the silence closed in again. All around, the bilberry plants were thick, and I ran my fingers through the stiff leaves, drawing off some of the small fruit that would dye my lips and teeth a deep purple. To the east, the hills rose up gradually to the sharp ridge where the pines stood. These trees spread away into Russia, into Asia, and for all I knew clean across the north to the ice-cold waters of the Bering Strait. To the west, the lake dwindled and became, suddenly, the river. A wooden bridge had been built here by the Lapps. I walked out over the stream and looked down into the clear water. There were fish there. I could see them lying dark against the sand, stemming the flow by weaving their tails with a sinuous grace. If my shadow passed across the surface, they would dart away, but were soon back at the old game.

Fishing was hardly sporting in that river. I do not expect it had been fished before, unless one considered the Lapp children who occasionally splashed around in the shallows, their rough birch rods trailing pieces of string towards the hungry but bewildered fish. I cast out into the rapids and at once saw the flash of fish as they came up to the fly. They seemed to relish the idea of being caught; they had not been pricked and played; they were quite unspoiled. By the time I left for the camp, I had ten grayling and three brown trout on my stick. Our friend the jay had a good breakfast that morning.

Back at the settlement, the family gathered round, verbose and smiling. In exchange for half a dozen fish, Mrs. Lenin gave me a loaf of bread, a few tiny potatoes and half a pint of warm, fresh milk. Across the lake, the smoke from our camp fire rose out from the trees and was white against the sky. The dogs ran along beside me and sniffed at the fish as I went down to the boat.

This settlement was self-contained. Each of the three log cabins had a great baking oven nearby, and there was a communal reindeer pen on the flat below the hills. The chief work of the men was simple; that of providing the means for their families' continued existence. They lived on the land, and their actual monetary turn-over was about five pounds annually. This was obtained through the sale of birch knife handles, wolf skins, gold dust from the river, and pemmican. During the summer months, their life was easy-going and pleasant, but the winters were hard and long and dark. The cabins were heated, but the fires smoked furiously, and the chimneys were barely more than holes in a corner of the roofs.

On that morning, I paused by the water's edge and sat down on a fallen tree. Laziness was deep in my bones. I was content to rest, to show the children my fly case with its gay colours, Butcher, Peter Ross, Grouse and Claret. This amused them, but their greatest joy was to find one of our old cigarette tins lying around. These tins had a certain value. Quite soon after our arrival there, we stopped flinging them into a pit behind the camp and began to bank them in our tents. As currency they were bulky but invaluable.

Lenin had taken his old rifle out across the lake. I could see his boat crawling over the flat water. As he approached a small island, we waited for the distant *ping* of his shot as he neatly drilled a duck. But, that day, he was out of luck. There was no rifle shot, and after a while our attention wandered to more immediate surroundings.

Between the cabins and the lake there was a cut patch of reeds. Like a field of fresh grass, this patch shone with a startling vividness. Scattered around were the family possessions. Just behind me, several spruce trunks leaned idly against one another. They were tipped and cleaned; they had some purpose, for here it was that the men sawed the long logs for the cabins, standing on the trestle, the great two-handed saw moving for hours on end. From the cabin walls hung fishing nets and drying pemmican and snowshoes. This was the summer scene, one of careful, intense preparation for the winter to come.

The reindeer were away on the tundra. In winter, they would be rounded up and used for hauling the sleighs down the Arctic highway; now they were far away and wild, stepping carefully through the cool darkness of the forests. In Lapland there were no frontiers. It was possible to wander into Norway or Sweden, Finland or Russia, without being stopped. This had certain drawbacks, for Russian soldiers were often met in the woods; ill-clad but well-armed, they would be looking for refugee Finns who had escaped from the boundaries of Soviet rule.

We were two hundred miles inside the Arctic Circle, but the sun was hot, its rays pouring down through such a clear atmosphere that our arms were tanned. Except for reindeer and a few wolves there were practically no animals up there.

C
17

It was young Lenin, aged twelve, who rowed me back to the camp. We asked him to stay to breakfast. He sat gravely beside the fire as we wrapped our fish in wet paper, pushing them into the wood embers. When the paper flaked off, the fish were cooked. We had some tea and sugar, enjoying the fresh milk that Mrs. Lenin had magically drawn from the fierce little cows. Young Lenin preferred the sweet stuff that oozed from the tin; he swallowed this raw, tipping back his head to let it roll down his throat. We watched, fascinated. When he left, he took the empty tin with him.

We left the camp and the lake and the Lapps on a bright morning when the sun was half-hidden by a high screen of misty white cloud. With prismatic compasses strapped to our wrists, groundsheets to act as tents, and a week's supply of food in our rucksacks, we walked lightly into the thin line of birch trees that hid what lay beyond. The ground was soft under our feet, and for the first hour the going was good. We lunched at the side of a small stream before following one of the hard reindeer tracks that meandered through the knee-high bilberry plants. It was all reminiscent of the Surrey hills or the Scottish glens. We almost forgot ourselves and expected that each clearing would reveal a tarmac road or an ice-cream man. But the nearest road was probably down on the western shores of Finmark, over a hundred miles ahead of us. There may have been ice-cream men around, but we did not see any.

During the afternoon, we met the first string of lakes. It did not worry us at first, but by nightfall we had not managed to find a way across, and were forced to camp in open ground, in the middle of a great bog. White, dead tree-trunks stood around like totem poles. Beneath the roots of one we lit our fire, and in no time the flames were licking skywards, following a black cloud of smoke that went up to cover the pale stars. In the little pools that surrounded us the fire danced brightly so that the whole scene was red and black and orange. Where the shadows lay, there was only a deep blackness.

Morning came slowly over the subdued glow of wood ash that lay between us. We started off early, but were soon checked by a swift flowing river, over fifty feet wide, black and deep under grass banks. We sat down on the bank and sucked our teeth. But the hills were still there, and they were definitely closer. We decided to walk down the river to Kaamanen where we could replenish our supplies, borrow a boat, and make a waterborne assault on the foothills. So that night the progressive postman's fair-haired daughter brought us cups of coffee while we bargained for a boat. The little village was quiet and peaceful under the shadows of the black pines, but to us it was like Piccadilly and Broadway lumped together. If we closed our eyes, the mosquito hum was like low-geared traffic. If we tried very hard, we could imagine that the sound of the river was from beneath Waterloo Bridge. But then our eyes were open, and we saw nothing but the few cabins and the evening sky darkening over the silence of the forest.

*   *   *

We were out on the river half an hour before sunset, the boat laden with provisions, a fishing-line over the stern. It was easy going at first, for the water was broad and deep, and we took it in turns to row. At the end of the first hour, we were clear of the pines and out among the birches. After sunset, the land was cheerless and chill, so we pulled into a small beach and unloaded the ground-sheets and sleeping-bags. Once the fire was going, the shadows of the night were banished. Overhead, a goose went up the river, wings sighing softly in the still air. The fish stopped playing in the pool below; they swam away to their secret night haunts. Lying on my back, warm within the wool-padded sleeping-bag, I could see the northern lights flickering across the brilliance of the stars. The sound of the river was very clear. As we listened, every splash and gurgle became separated from the general noise of moving water. We began to recognise the sound of each eddy and knew when a log floated past or when a duck arrived with a flurry on the surface. Shortly before I slept, I remembered, with satisfaction, the boat that lay on the sand below. There would be no marching for a few days. We would be able to give our boots a rest.

That river went up into the hills for many miles, and for us each mile was more difficult than the last. Often, we had to push the boat up rapids and were sometimes forced to carry most of our provisions along the bank. One day we came round a bend to see rapids rising above us in an unending flight of rearing steps. This in fact was no surprise, for creeping along in the morning sunlight we had heard the distant murmur and had seen the shining patches of foam that floated past and were always the heralds of rough going. This particular rapid had worried us two days before we came to it. For one thing, the hills were not now far ahead, and it was obvious that something would have to happen before long. Had the river turned to follow the northward curve of the valley, all would have been well. As it was, we had to haul the boat up under the trees and go the rest of the way on foot.

Once again, therefore, we began the business of trying to walk in a straight line. But many hours were spent finding a way between the incessant strings of lakes. Our road might appear to be open until the very last moment, and then as we moved cautiously forward the blue water would shine between the branches. And then it was a question of tossing a coin. To east or to west? Right or left? Heads or tails?

One morning, making our way through a small valley, we came across a party of nomadic Lapps. They squatted beside a stream, complete with skin tents, dogs, children, ancient guns and hunks of pemmican. They did not seem surprised to see us and made room beside the wood fire. In the evening, one of the younger men picked up a rifle and we joined him in his search for duck. It was nearly September, and the birch leaves were turning a brilliant yellow; the sky was pale but clear; the waters of a circular lake were solid in immobility. We walked away from the chatter of the children and soon there was only the deep silence, into which the passing of our feet over moss fell in a rhythmic whisper. Far away, across the northern slopes, the reindeer wandered in long lines, white rectangles against the grey-green of the bilberry plants. In the centre of the lake there was a small island. The Lapp pointed out over the water and led us down to where his boat lay under the steep bank. We rowed him out, moving slowly into the scarlet reflection of sunset.

There were plenty of duck round the island. We could see them moving into the reeds. I was up in the bows, watching the water curl away from beneath the boat, when the gun went off with a vicious crack behind my ear. At once the air was full of birds, but there was one that flapped and struggled in the water. The Lapp grinned in a frenzy of excitement. By the time we had recovered the bird from where it floated in the shadows, there was a deep blue light over the hills and lake and stream. We could see the camp fire, a red pin-point of light to guide us home.

It was a peaceful row back. The oars dipped regularly; the twin bow waves went out in a gigantic V, long narrow lines that reached the distant shores. It was growing cold, and clouds were covering the stars. A faint wind stirred the branches of the trees. Then abruptly we were back at the camp and the fire was close. The children ran down to meet us, their laughter loud and their teeth shining.

Next morning, I awoke to find the snow coming through the crisp birch leaves. It rustled softly with a sound that came and went in our ears like the murmur of a distant train. It was time we moved off. We had been warned that the second fall might be heavy, and we had no wish to be caught in the open country with no tents. Two days later we reached the place where we had left our boat. Safe from the snows, we camped there for two days, idling away the time and preparing for the journey downstream. There was plenty to do. There were fish to catch. We shot a goose and some other birds whose skins we kept for the base-camp ornithologist. Our boots had to be oiled, clothes washed, firewood collected and food cooked. Every hour that we wasted, lying on our backs and watching the thin, white clouds passing behind a screen of yellow leaves, had to be made up later.

It had taken us a week to make our way upstream. We went down in two days, careering along at the speed of the river, one

oar over the stern to guide us clear of the most obvious rocks. Once
we grounded with a bang, but the boat survived. Once one of us
fell overboard and was recovered from the shadows of a deep pool
into which he had been swept. The second day was more peaceful,
for the river broadened, and we could sit at ease and watch the
country move past. We reached the pine belt, the trees standing
black above white boulders, their branches etched against the sky.
When at length we ran on to the beach at Kaamanen, it was like a
summer's evening. The postman was away, but the dogs welcomed
us. We relaxed within four wooden walls while the flies danced in
the window and the dust rose through the beams of sunlight.
Suddenly, a telephone rang harshly in the next room. We were
back in the world again.

*   *   *

My memories of Lapland are clear, quite apart from those of other
countries. I can still see the almost flat land, its stunted birch as
yellow as a canary, the pine trees standing above white boulders, the
little cabins and the patches of emerald-green reed. The reindeer
helped to make the place unlike any other and gave it a fairy-tale
atmosphere. Out on the edge of the wide, flat swamps, we saw
rough crosses standing about like dead trees. They were not small,
but stood ten or twelve feet above the bilberry leaves. And then
there were the Siberian jays and the willow grouse. Lapland was
more than a wild spot with hills and rivers and lakes; it seemed to
cast its spell, for the little men were still up there. The nomads
have their strange, secret rites. The land is one of witch and
goblin.

We left in the early autumn when the low hills shone like brass
and the lakes were a clear, vivid blue. We left before the snow
came, but for some imagination saw the small huts covered by fall
after fall of thick snow. The lake would be black with ice and then
a slate grey. The paths would vanish. The long night would creep
down and the northern lights would shine on the ice far above.

That was a picture in our mind. We saw our Lapp friends shutting out the winter gales and rolling into their rough bunks to close their eyes and listen to the wind and feel the heat of the wood fire on their faces. It would be in the winter that they had time to think of what had passed and what might come. We from civilisation had entered into their small world, learning much and finding a fundamental goodness amongst them. What had they benefited from our visit? Shining empty cigarette tins were all they had to remember us by. When the tins rusted and were flung out, they would remember no more.

CHAPTER THREE

MOUNTAIN AND VALLEY

THE farmhouse stood on the north side of the Spey valley; it looked across the trees that screened the river to rising cornfields, purple hills and distant blue mountains. Behind the house a woody glen ran up through the moors. About four hundred yards to the west of the main farm buildings stood an old mill towards which one of the small brown streams had been diverted to turn the creaking mill-wheel. The mill itself was almost symbolic, for it indicated an age and a way of life. Everything was leisurely. The ploughs moved no faster than the old horse. The mill-wheel groaned round with a weary reluctance. Old George, the farmer, plodded from one field to another with the heavy roll of a sailor; he was getting old, and was very much a part of the scenery. He lived in a stone cottage that lay between a thick bank of trees and a stream. Down there it was almost always dark, and autumn mists lay heavy along the water.

George managed the farm entirely by himself. At the time the mill was still working he had one horse, six cows, about a hundred hens and ducks and turkeys, two peacocks and a sow. The harvested fields lay up the glen, divided by stone walls and screens of silver birch. In September he hired a reaper to do his cutting, but the wheat was gathered in by hand and horse-drawn cart, taken to the mill, ground and bagged, and then delivered in the same old cart. Sometimes George would set off at dawn, the black horse ambling slowly down to the road, bound for Bridge of Brown or Tomintoul, away across the hills. He would be lucky if he was back by midnight, but the crofters had their sack of wheat and that was what mattered.

The old mill was breath-taking. The inside was very dark, wooden wheels vaguely visible, and leather bands connecting one part of the antique machinery to another. There had once been a fire there, and the smell of burning was always in the cold damp air.

The whiteness of flour was thick over everything including the many near-wild cats that had made their home in the dark corners.

It was the river that dominated the valley, sometimes by sudden floods or low water, sometimes by fury or tranquillity, but always by its aid to the valley's fertility and its constant swift flowing. It was only a short walk from the farm to the river. The track crossed a wooden bridge, meandered down the banks of a stream, and climbed up through a hillock. From there it was possible to see the water shining below, and if it was evening, to hear the salmon jumping in the pools. There were a great many fish in the Spey, salmon, sea-trout and brown trout, as well as pike and eels, but to catch them was not easy. I bought a licence to enable me to fish the club waters, oiled my rods, made up lines, and went down to study the evening fly. At length, after all the vital and enjoyable preparation, I turned my back on old George who was touching up one of the carts with indigo blue, and wandered down across the fields to the water's edge.

It was mid-August. The evening light was strong but mellow. The river was low through lack of rain, but in the deeper pools the trout were rising regularly. Behind me, the birch trees shone green; they were very beautiful, but I grew to hate them, for many of my best new flies caught on the high branches and were lost for ever. Not being an expert fisherman, I expected to land something during that first evening. But, needless to say, I came home empty-handed. I knew an English clergyman who fished the Spey every year, every day of every year. He used to stay out half the night, wading in the darkness that covered the treacherous currents. But he hardly ever caught anything. But, I used to tell myself, he was after salmon, whereas I would be happy to bring back a half-pound brown trout.

After a week of fruitless walking and casting and changing my fly, I decided to enlist help. So it was that I first met Tommy Grant. His reputation was violent. It was said that he drank too much, was rarely sober in fact, and was openly dishonest and dirty. But no one denied that Tommy knew more about the Spey waters between

25

Garton Bridge and Castle Grant than any man alive. His life had been adventurous, and he used to tell me about it as we sat in the smoke of a wood fire, watching the water glide past and waiting for the trout to start rising. He had done nothing exceptional, but his stories were from a new angle. Whether in the trenches or with the Black and Tans, he seemed to have accomplished a little less or a little more, depending on his mood, than those around him. Now, his wandering days over, he lived in a shack near the railway station, poaching salmon for a living and bicycling twenty-five miles to Inverness to sell fish at hotel back-doors.

I first met Tommy outside the bar of the Palace Hotel. He came out into the summer twilight, weaving about like a full-rigged ship with a broken rudder. His tweed cap was well down over his eyes and the air around him was thick with the scent of raw whisky. I stood in his path and he regarded me as if I were a distant mountain.

"I've two split cane trout rods," I said, "and a licence to fish the club waters. But I don't have any luck. What's the secret?"

He put out one hand to steady himself and the corners of his lips twitched. "Be at the churchyard," he said dreamily, "at eight o'clock to-morrow night." And then he slipped past me and vanished into the shadows.

That was all. I hadn't much hope when I carried my gear down to the river bank the following night. Behind me, the old walled churchyard was deserted. The trees were very still against a pink sky. There was a breathless silence, and it was possible to hear the ratchet of a reel as an unseen fisherman moved patiently upstream on the opposite bank. Then, with a noise like a pistol shot, a salmon flicked the surface below me. By the time my head had turned there was nothing to be seen but the widening circles.

I sat on the top of a stile and waited. Presently, footsteps sounded down the sandy road and Tommy appeared. He seemed to be walking steadily. A long piece of grass stuck from between his lips, and he eyed the river with a strange arrogance.

In appearance, Tommy was like Popeye the Sailor. He had the same rubber cheeks. In place of the pipe there was always a stick of

26

grass. He had a way of smacking his lips and compressing them over toothless gums. But it was not his appearance that mattered, for he had the manner of a Grand Duke. He was the only man I have ever met who had a healthy contempt for nature and was able to use the land as a god might. He respected his fellow men with a faintly ironical over-emphasis, but his politeness was worth watching. He might live in a shack, reek of whisky, have a reputation on both sides of the Grampians, but he could have taught many a fine English gentleman the art of deportment and unselfconsciousness.

On that first evening we walked in single file, because of the narrowness of the path, up the river's edge to Tarrig Mhor. Tommy strolled ahead, plucking straws as he went, not offering to carry the rods. He was very sober, and his eyes were as bright as the evening light on the river. We came to the pool when the sun was slipping behind the hills. There was no one near. Except for some small black cows moving in the shallows below the opposite bank, nothing moved. Tommy sat down on the bank and accepted one of my cigarettes. "Well," he said, in his soft Scottish voice. "Now we'll see." He made up one rod while I tackled the other. He never complained that my lines were cheap and my flies but few. He never sucked his teeth over the fact that one of the rods had been broken and was crudely mended so that it had lost most of its suppleness. It was a case of "Now we'll see," and he'd be off along the bank, his straw at an acute angle with his nose, his heavy boots moving with uncanny delicacy in the reeds.

I moved upstream and Tommy went down towards the shallow water at the bend. There was always a tense excitement about the first cast of the evening, but on that occasion I felt doubly pleased with life. The shadows were creeping in and a soft blue haze was falling like rain on to the trees and fields and water. Out of the corner of my eye, I watched Tommy choose his spot, set his feet, and send his line out into the current. His cast was easy and unspectacular, almost casual. He was not, I discovered, an expert in the delicate art of fly fishing, not, at any rate, when it was a matter of hooking fish against their will. Tommy's approach was much more thorough and far more scientific. For instance, he knew where the fish were, and refused to try a single cast until the sun was just right, and the flies were dancing on the surface. He knew every rock on the river bottom, partly from dangerous paddling and partly from taking careful note of the bed that was revealed during exceptional drought. There was, too, something uncanny about the way he made use of the habits of the fish. He seemed to know just what frightened a salmon, made it angry, or lured it from the shadow of a rock.

Tommy did not stay long in each pool. There was something incredibly confident about the way he seemed to expect immediate results. I moved away from him until he was nearly out of sight, then reeling in my line, walked downstream to watch him from the bank. Within five minutes of my arrival he had a trout on his line. He did not turn and show any pleasure, but played the fish for a while before hauling it in to the bank and bending down to grasp the cast. The trout shone in the last of the day's sunlight. Tommy glanced up at me and pressed his lips together. "Just a wee one," he said. "'Tis a bit early . . ."

He caught three more before we packed up and went home, the last in a flurry of splashing in the darkness. I said good night where our roads divided, mine to the farm and his to the old shack where he spent his nights. As we stood there, he looked up at the stars and said: "They're a good long way off."

"True."

"It must be cold out there of a night," said Tommy thoughtfully, and he went off down the road, whistling softly to himself.

The farm was shining white in the clarity of the night. Behind, the hills were solid and black, wrapped in a hollow silence. The slate roof of the old mill shone like a lake at midday.

Tommy Grant had a secret but most important private life. I never discovered what he did during the days when he vanished into the blue. He would return without explanation, and I knew that questions would be unanswered. He was no man's servant. He

28

helped me with my fishing because he liked the feel of a rod, and, I think, because he liked helping me, or anyone else.

When the drought continued, and the river was little more than a thin white ripple over the rocks, we packed our gear and went off over the moors to Lochan Dhorb. The loch was almost rectangular, a mile by half a mile, with a ruined castle on an island in the middle. Here we fished from a boat, rowing out over the blue water and drifting in the morning sunlight while our lines snaked out and the brown trout mounted in the basket. On occasions, we were joined by friends for a picnic lunch. Tommy was never put out by the laughter of the girls; he opened gates with an easy grace, lay flat on his back in the heather while the rest of us carried the hampers ashore, and made a fire to protect himself from the midges, the smoke of which drifted over us as well. He helped some of us into the boats, but did not offer to row. He tied casts, but was indifferent to a hat that unhappily fell overboard. The unending stream of his charm flowed through the afternoon hours.

There is no clear-cut rule to tell us where sportsmanship begins and ends. Certainly, sportsmanship has little to do with the regulations laid down in club licence cards. I would say, rather, that it is inseparable from skill. Netting salmon is less skilful than catching them with fly, line and rod, and therefore less sporting. Tommy Grant's many ways of catching fish never lacked skill, and I was never to feel that we were cheating.

The summer idled by, one of those Scottish summers that are full of contrast, rain following sun, the mountains soft at one moment and bleak and hard at the next. The water turned from grey to blue. Sometimes the Spey was a deep thick brown, almost like coffee. Sometimes it was as clear as white glass. Tommy taught me how to make minnow out of odds and ends; he always used his own make. His subtle fingers whipped the break in my rod and made the whole as good as new. We plodded over the paths that skirted the cornfields, discovering new pools and new rapids. We drove over the pass to a deep stream, below eroded rock, where the trout hovered under sheer falls, presenting immense problems if we hooked one of them. Towards the end of August, Tommy disappeared on one of his mysterious journeys. By the time he returned, the weather had changed, and a cool wind was blowing down the valley from the west, whipping up the river and flicking through the ripening crops. It rained at night, not heavily, but with a quick, driving splatter that was from a racing cloud. For the most part, the sky remained clear.

One evening, as I came down through the deep blue shadows of the farmyard, I saw a figure standing on the edge of a field looking up at the sky. It was obvious who it was.

"Hello, Tommy," I said. "It's going to rain."

He continued to look up for a while, and then his feet moved softly through the grasses. "'Tis a good night for a salmon."

"To-night?"

"Aye. There's been rain on the hills all day. It should be down here by now. The river'll be up."

"All right," I said. "Let's go."

We walked in silence down to the black pines that stood back from the grass banks. The wind shivered the branches and flicked cold drops of water down on us. Under our feet, the ground was soft and slippery. As we approached, I could hear the murmur of the water, the song of a thousand ripples and the dull whisper of the Spey's relentless speed.

We passed clear of the trees and came down to the edge of the water. At once, it was obvious that Tommy was right. The river had risen. The sand of a small beach, snow-white in the diffused starlight, was only a thin strip below the bank. The surface was covered with branches and leaves and thick bunches of twigs. The wind was gusty; it passed through the birch leaves with a sound of fierce discord and swept down the river, unimpeded. Two oyster-catchers flew upstream, into the teeth of the blast, their regular and plaintive call reaching us intermittently. Tommy moved into the black shadows of the wooden shelter; he lit a cigarette, and his shadow sprang out from the gold glimmer of the match flame. He was being reticent and cautious, and I knew, therefore, that something was afoot. The river watcher, Tommy's old enemy, would be on the prowl on such a night. I had a feeling of confidence, for it was unlikely that we would be on the same bank as the law. Tommy's planning was too complete for that.

But there was plainly an expectation in his attitude. He produced some things from his pocket and bent over them while I made up the rods. A narrow black cloud raced overhead. A flutter of rain passed over the water. There was a quiet then, a pause in the bluster of the night. It seemed as if the light was brighter, for the rocks shone out with a vague whiteness.

"Prawn," Tommy said suddenly. I bent close, and could smell the tweed of his threadbare jacket, a richness of age and smoke and natural things like old wood, heather and dried casts. Between the circle of his curved fingers, I could see the prawn, a pale shape above three large hooks. The bait took shape, but I had to wait a while for explanation. Then, at length, Tommy held it up and chuckled. "That should do it."

"Do salmon like them?"

"No. They hate 'em," Tommy said seriously, and he went on to outline his strategy. It seemed that salmon were temperamental. They disliked uncertain, windy nights. They were inclined to lie in the shadows of rocks and sulk. Nothing, no fly, no minnow would draw them out. But, if touched by anything, they would turn and snap. Tommy picked up the spinning rod, swung it round his head in the manner of a soldier with a sword, and crouched to wind on the lead weights. He moved lithely and confidently, his actions based on years of experience. I knew that when he next stood up we would be ready, and was filled with an immense excitement. There was, I think, something more than anticipation of catching a salmon, or the thrill of illicit means. Successful poaching, in fact, was not the main reason for enchantment. It was Tommy's presence that mattered, his soft charm, his natural blending of thought and action. That night he was fulfilling his twin functions as a man.

About a hundred yards upstream from the shelter, the river curved sharply to the north, the main stream flowing under the shadows of the right bank. On our side, a neck of sand and gravel ran out a good way from the trees. It was dry underfoot, dry and hard and rough. We crunched our way over the paleness, stepping carefully to avoid the larger rocks. Out there, the force of the wind was direct, and we felt its impact on our wrists as it struck the thin lengths of the rods that leaned away like young saplings.

Tommy whistled a few bars, then he said: "You have first go. You may need more weights in this breeze."

"Where are the fish?" I asked.

He glanced up at the sky as if to seek inspiration. "Just wait a while. There's a spot of rain coming down from Nethy Bridge."

We stood there, side by side, silent. I was shivering with the cold. A quarter of a mile behind us, the pines reared like a black sea. The river came out of the night and was near us, swift and glinting, and then we lost sight of it as it swept to the south. Ten minutes later a flicker of hard rain pattered on our bowed shoulders. Tommy's feet moved on the shingle. I swung the rod back, eased the ratchet on the reel, and tried the weight of the line. It seemed all right at first. My arms jerked forward. The tip of the rod flew through an arc, and the bait sailed out into the wind. I did not see a splash, but almost at once the line was tugging from downstream and I began to reel in.

"Too light," Tommy said. "Any more weights?"

"One."

"Good."

We put on the last length of lead. I tried another cast and saw the bait fall far out in the half-darkness. Tommy grunted approval. Very gently, he took the rod from me and began to haul the line in by hand in a series of short jerks. His eyes were turned upstream, and presently he straightened up, the bait swinging back against the stars. I crouched down and saw the slow swing of his shoulders. The line went singing through the eyelets. There was a moment of great stillness and then his left forearm began to haul in again. He seemed to have forgotten my presence. His mind was out there on the river, out there below the dark surface, picturing the shape of the rocks and the path of the strongest current. He was drawing on his memories as a man might draw on a depth of wisdom. He was supreme as he stood there, as casual as could be, as clear-minded as one who had not had a drink for years, as strong as a great tree. His cap was well down over his eyes. His coat collar was turned up against the rain and wind. His feet were planted squarely on the stones.

Motionless, I grew steadily colder. The gusts seemed more and more ferocious. The river was a mass of spitting wavelets which hissed and flicked against the bank. The rain shot into my face like steel pellets. For a minute, perhaps more, I could see and hear nothing, and then the cloud passed and the stars were out again, blue and vivid. On their long reflections I saw the rod. It was no longer a supple line, but curved downwards with a rock-like steadiness. I stumbled to my feet and clutched Tommy's arm. "You have one?"

He grinned and nodded. For a moment I felt ridiculous. He treated the whole thing as an affair of the greatest simplicity, taking his time, getting the feel of the fish.

That was the start of it. The dial of my luminous watch showed that it was half-past twelve. Far up the valley, the sky was pale and clear. The mountains were little more than a skyline; they might have been any height, any distance from us. The cornfields showed up, disembodied by the flickering starlight.

Tommy walked very slowly down the edge of the water, six steps that brought him to the end of the spit. I heard his reel clicking. Already, it seemed, he was hauling in the fish, and then the rod twanged and the line sang out again. He chuckled. "A good fish. I'm well in him."

"Salmon?"

He nodded. "Aye. And a fair weight."

I felt rather weak. The rod was meant for trout and the line was old and short and thin in places where it had snagged around rocks. We had neither gaff nor net.

The fish had gone downstream. Tommy was stepping in the water

D

and I saw him cast a quick glance behind him, judging the best way to move if he had a chance. Everything seemed to pause. The salmon was a dead weight; the rod bent at a vicious curve; the soles of Tommy's boots were firm in the mud. Soon something was bound to move. The tension was immense.

Then, with a terrific run, the salmon came up towards us; it leaped clear of the water once, a silver streak. The reel sang as fast as Tommy's wrist could turn. The angle of the rod changed and the curve whipped up and down like a blade of grass in a hurricane.

"D'you see yon?" Tommy said, grinning from ear to ear. "I thought he was hanging me up."

The line flicked across the water, and a flicker of white showed in the darkness under the far bank. Once again, the night was quite still. Nothing moved but the rippling surface. I could hear the ticking of my watch. Tommy moved his feet about six inches and sniffed musically. He seemed to be settling down to a long fight.

Once, during the next two hours, that salmon came in close under our feet. I saw him as he rushed through the shallows, a curved streak of white with a hint of length and breadth in the shadow around. Once he went racing upstream until there could have been only a few feet of line on the reel.

The end came abruptly. At one moment the rod was arched and steady, the line taut to the surface on which it caused a tiny whirl-pool. And then, without warning, everything was slack and Tommy began to reel in with a barely perceptible lift of his shoulders. "He's awa'."

My acute disappointment was mixed with a certain relief. The tension had been far greater for me. I had been the one to doubt, to count each minute, to watch but not to feel. Tommy glanced at the end of the line and whistled tunelessly through his teeth. Bait and cast had vanished.

"Care to try again?" he asked.

"No," I said. "I don't think so. Not to-night . . . this morning."

He understood, and we packed up the things. We were silent as we went up the road between the pine trees, a road that was white under the stars. I was thinking how futile was my cheap rod, how inferior the thin line, how inadequate the box of flies. When our ways parted, I merely said "Good night," and turned away.

"'Twas a good fish," Tommy said quietly. "We could have had him, you know, if we had had a net. . . ."

I looked across to the black shape of the mountains and knew, suddenly, that I would not return to the river for a day or two. Disappointment could be washed out on the peaks where there was always a gale blowing and where the snow lay hard in between the rocks. Up there, on the roof of the world, it was possible to look across to the western highlands while below the great rivers were minute threads of blue, weaving delicately between the summer green. Up there, perspective triumphed.

*   *   *

The Grampian mountains, wild and frightening, yet possessing a soft beauty of their own, are the highest and most impressive range in the British Isles. True, they are a few feet lower than the peak of Ben Nevis, but they do not fade away below the clouds, but spread from one horizon to the other. They drew, as mountains always will, a string of keen climbers. They had their mysteries and their tragedies. Near the foot of the Lairig pass there was a cold heap of stones, the grave of a young man who had been caught in the hills by the grey mists, the thick mists that come down in the late evenings. He had lost his way, stumbled down over the rocks and clumps of heather, terrified, dead weary. When found, he was barely a few yards from the path that would have led him to safety.

The Range had its ghosts, some pleasant and friendly, others black and desolate. There was a black-coated man with an umbrella supposed to haunt the top of Cairngorm. There was the giant who followed the unwary, an echo, perhaps, footsteps behind the man who hurried down in the gathering darkness. The summits, Cairngorm, Ben Macdhui, Brae-Riach, Cairn Toul, are all vast and individual. In their deep passes once lived the northern Picts. At the time of Christ, the Picts huddled here, awaiting attack, living and dying in their last hideouts. Their ghosts must be up there too.

A day in the Cairngorms is never without interest. It is a long walk from the end of the rough road to the summit, a slow and steady climb. Always there is the urge that drives men on to the highest peaks, but there are other things as well. On the left, a river runs from the pass, its water is a clear white, like spilled glass. Red deer run in the shadows of the trees. There are ptarmigan and grouse and wild cat.

I went up by way of the Lairig pass. The path winds between high, steep slopes, a clean cut in the mountains. The skyline is so high on either side that one is apt to forget the sky and the sunlight. Here I could see the ghosts of the little men with their stone weapons. I could talk to them and listen to the wind in reply. I could close my eyes and see them moving off to the hunt or squatting by the peat fires with the rain chilling their backs.

About noon, I left the side of the stream and started to climb the eastern slope. High above the sun bathed the heather and shone on the thin leaves of the stunted birches. Higher still the rocks stood out against the sky. The peak was hidden, the goal invisible. Under my feet, the flat stones slipped away and fell. The last of the pines leaned precariously from between two boulders; its roots were like a family of snakes, its branches spread towards the light like the flat hands of an Egyptian dancer. That tree was half-way up the slope, two hundred feet above the path, two hundred feet from the skyline. It was forlorn and lonely, fighting a losing battle against the mountain storms.

Once over the crest, it was I who was alone. Mine was the only shadow up there. A little stream, clear as crystal, ran through the heather. Turning, I looked towards the north, out over the width of the valley, over the hilltops, over the white clouds that hung low over the Moray Firth. The Spey was three thousand feet below, indicating its path by a thin line of green between the pale fields. A road twisted from the foothills, a white thread, winding and dipping amid the darkness of the forests.

On the upper slopes, it was very still, painfully silent. There was not the usual half gale. It was possible to hear the whisper of a stream long after the water had been passed. The call of grouse or ptarmigan echoed out over the pass and returned, faint and shrill. Far over to the west, I could see a herd of red deer moving over the skyline. They must have been on the slopes of Ben Macdhui, coming down from the cold. Perhaps they were making for the small conical hill that lies at the entrance to the pass and is their own sanctuary. No shot is heard on that hill, no hunter disturbs its peace.

To reach the top of a mountain is terrifically satisfying. Once Everest is climbed, a certain glamour will depart from the world, and considering all things, it might be best if that peak were left well alone. The bottom of the Pacific and the top of Everest will remain aloof while man is born and perishes within a brief moment. Should they be easily conquered, it is probable that man will turn his attention to the universe, to the moon, the planets and the stars. The climb must go on.

I walked away from the sharp edge of the pass. Once the view was lost, the atmosphere became more remote. The flat stretch below the summit was apart from the whole world. The silence throbbed; the sun beat down through dustless air; the sound of my nailed shoes on rock was as brittle as rifle fire. I went on slowly, not hurrying, for the sky looked clear to north and south and east. Far over the western ridge there was a thin layer of cloud, but it seemed motionless and harmless.

You do not have to climb the Grampian peaks. One could, if interested, take a rope and scale the inner side of the steep corries, but that would be no more useful than climbing up the side of one of the valley farmhouses. No. The top of the Cairngorm is reached by steady and untiring walking. It is, perhaps, in the descent that strength is needed. Old ground is passed once more. The trees are reached and the sandy path goes on ahead, curve after curve, wooden bridges, rises and twists, shadow and light. In the cool of evening the gate is reached beyond which the cars stand, and very welcome they are too. The whole walk might be a matter of fifteen miles, all up or down hill. That is the test of the peaks.

The summit of Cairngorm was at the head of a long gradual slope. A small cairn of stones indicated the highest point. There was little to see. All around, the brown slopes were like rugged velvet in the soft sunlight. The valleys were hidden by a thin white mist. The cloud to the west had closed in on the top of Ben Macdhui. Suddenly I began to fear the evening and did not stay long up there. While the sun was strong on my shoulders, it seemed absurd to be alarmed, but that mist, far below, might rise in my face and be dangerous. The second threat might creep down from above. Once the light faded and the heat died the deep angles between the hills would be smothered in a curling, creeping vapour, blinding and thick.

I went down fast. My feet slithered on the dead heather. Ahead, below, the steep slopes ran down to distant foothills and the forest stretched away to the farmlands. The shadows between the patches of sunlight were a thick, cold blue. It was possible to feel them, as if swimming through layers of cool water. I passed half-remembered landmarks; the stump of a long-dead tree, the grey-white bones of a deer, the great rock on the side of which moss was a rich scarlet. Behind, the clouds came down over the peaks, covering them one by one, as relentless as the last folding of a shroud over the face of a loved one.

I hurried on. A flicker of wind was moaning in the pine trees far below. Their murmur was the only sound and I felt far from the world, too damned far from the guiding path. The sun was only just above the western skyline. Its evening heat was holding the mists at bay for me. When it had gone there would be no brake.

I did not return the same way, avoiding the bottom of the pass and keeping to the slopes as long as possible. It was when I was rounding a level shoulder, following a slight path in the thick heather, that I heard a brisk sound of footsteps behind me. This was no ghost, no terror. I turned my head and saw a half-grown deer trotting along in my wake, its nose about two feet from my elbow. It seemed quite unconcerned, apparently convinced that I was a part of the herd. Its eyes met mine with a trustful stare. We went on together until quite suddenly the flank of the moving herd appeared close. My little friend paused, puzzled. It eyed me in doubt, and then flicked its heels into the earth and was off and away. I saw the mother come out and retrieve it. And then the whole herd moved off at a trot and were soon out of sight.

I knew my way down the foothills. It was quite simple. One had only to keep along the right bank of the white Einich river, cross by a fallen pine, and strike up a steep slope near the conical deer sanctuary and reach the path down to the deer gate. It was, as I say, quite simple. But when I reached the ridge from which I could look down over the river the whole scene was like the sea in winter, flat and grey and dotted with black islands. The mist was rising. Behind me, it was sweeping along the slopes like a blizzard, moving fast, wreathing and clinging like smoke on glass. I took a few quick bearings and plunged downward. The sun dipped. It was cold and the air was keen in my lungs.

All the way down, growing more and more tired, always hoping for the sound of the river, I was plagued by superstition, half-listening over my shoulder for the steps of the giant, the echoes that drove the sense out of a man and made him desert the path for mad short cuts in the half-darkness. But when I stopped to ease my heaving breath, the silence was complete. The light seemed to be draining away all too fast. I thought of the mile or two to go to the river and then the four-mile walk down through the black and empty forest. It was a question of slipping and sliding downwards, always downwards. The river was right at the bottom. That was the one thing I did know.

That fallen tree spanning the stream had, when I was on the distant summit, seemed so very near home, but when I reached it it was only a milestone, a thankful sight but not giving any long rest to my legs. I was still far above the road which came up from the valley, and the mist was swirling through the trees. But it took only a few minutes to scramble up to the path and then I just set my legs in motion and hummed a march and half-closed my eyes and went on. Once or twice I glanced over my shoulder and looked up at the clouded mountain tops. It looked cold and bleak and remote up there and I thanked God I wasn't still near the cairn and wondered what in heaven's name had drawn me up there in the first place.

It was raining a fine grey rain in the lower hills. The birch leaves glittered and the silver trunks were like soft silver. The half-light was thick, and I stumbled on unseen holes and rocks. In half an hour, it would be quite dark and there was no sign of a star. There would be no light at all, not a glimmer to keep me out of the forest. Those last four miles turned and twisted and every corner looked like the last. This was the time when the deep shadows were cheerless and forbidding and I would have given all I possessed for the sight of a distant light and the sound of a car or a train or . . .

And then I was suddenly there. I could not see the car yet, but there was the dark glow of a fire and someone called out, and not far away shone a glimmer from the crofter's cottage and there was the friendly excited barking of my dog. It was one of the small, fast-forgotten moments which make all things seem worth-while. So indeed was the drive back across the wide moors and the sight of the white farmhouse with its lights streaming into the garden and a warmth within and a long night of sleep and the clear morning when one looked out and saw the peaks away across the valley and knew that they were friends after all.

*   *   *

September brought strength and colour to the valley; it was a month of ecstasy, for the rowans turned scarlet, the heather was redder and the birch leaves began to have their canary-yellow edges. The crops were like golden stretches of sea, gusted and windblown, and the river came up in a swift flood after the rains. The sound of the river was deep above the light winds, and the water glimmered wide and blue between the trees. Often the mornings were shivered by quick winds but most of the evenings were quiet and still and bathed in a warm sun.

This was the time we collected our old spinning rods, dug a tin of worms from the farmyard and went down to the water's edge with sandwiches and beer. There was one place that I favoured above all others. A small stream came in from the north and between it and the river there was a small spit of sand. Here I used to go, propping my rod on a stick and lying back in the sun, watching the sparkle of the water over the top of my shoes. It was lazy fishing, like that of the "Brighton Pier" school, but the surroundings were perfect and the sea trout we caught were the ones that had evaded our flies for so long. Not far down the path there was a remote and walled churchyard. I don't know whether the morbid connection between the graves and worms and fish had anything to do with the value of that particular part of the bank, but the fish were always there.

Tommy Grant enjoyed worm fishing. It suited him, for he could lie as flat as a fallen tree, his piece of grass jutting out from the stubble on his chin, his blue eyes watching the white clouds pass. When the fish nibbled and the rod ends jumped up and down, he would put out a weary arm and give the line a tug. If the fish was hooked he'd nod to me and take no further part in the proceedings. We used to lunch on a patch of warm pine needles, sometimes making a fire and boiling water for tea and grilling a fresh trout in the wood embers. There was no hurry. The river would go on flowing and the sun would set and rise and the rain would continue to fall high up in the hills. Our consciences were as clear as the September air, and I used to think of very ordinary, simple things—of the wild flowers along the bank, of the salmon who came from far-off Norway, of the birds who flew swiftly up the stream, or of the character of a man who could be seen in the distance cutting a small field of wheat with a scythe. There was, too, the fascination of the river. It looked so innocent and blue and gay, yet it could be cruel and treacherous. It claimed at least one life a year. I remembered the two young boys who had died in the flood the year before, their bodies washed down to the shallows far below, their coffins lying in their croft-home for days while their parents refused to let them be taken away. The river had its tragedies.

About the middle of September, Tommy had to leave. The police were making inquiries, for it seemed he had offended in some way or other. And so he vanished, took to the hills to live on the land with the deer and the hare and the wildcat. He took one of my rods with him. I did not care. The fishing was almost over, and we had enjoyed our months by many waters. Wherever he went, I wished him a very good season. I did not worry about his living up in the wind and rain of the hills and forests, for he had never lived artificially, never forgotten the nature from which we are all descended. He was lucky. I often wonder how many of us would survive if circumstances forced mankind back to his native woods. There would indeed be a sad harvest.

CHAPTER FOUR

THE MAGELLANIC CLOUDS

IN 1939 a substantial portion of the world's produce was carried from place to place in sailing vessels. There were Greek caiques, Portuguese schooners, junks, barges, feluccas and square-rigged ships. There were German barques, and there was the Finnish fleet of steel, ocean-going barques owned by Captain Gustav Erikson of Mariehamn, Aaland Islands. About fifteen of his ships made the long voyage from South Australia to Europe every year. It was in one of his ships, the four-master *Viking*, that I returned to England during late spring and early summer of 1938.

I had left school some two years before, with a series of disjointed ambitions. I was determined to visit both the Arctic and Antarctic circles, to climb Mount Everest, to round the Horn in a sailing ship, to write a best-seller, to have a letter published in *The Times*. The first, the crossing of the Arctic circle, was behind me. The Erikson fleet, provided I did not delay, could still provide ships for the Cape Horn route. It was only a question of finding the ships and paying passage money, an apprentice premium, or, if lucky, signing on a short-handed vessel as a seaman. In London, I had been told that there were difficulties to be faced. It was far easier to join as one of the crew in Australia, for some of the Finns were inclined to desert into the snowless land, and captains were pleased to have cheap labour in lieu. It was, of course, always possible to pay the apprentice premium, but in any case I had missed the outward-bound ships and would have to make my own way to Australia unless I wanted to wait for another year. Before leaving England, I had paid the agents a sum which would ensure that, if I could not sign on, I would be in a position to demand an apprentice's berth.

I travelled out in a cargo vessel; a long two months of sea and sun; a landless vista; the eternal blue ahead with the hot decks and the throb of the propeller. And then, abruptly, came the impact of Australia.

Australia has its own atmosphere, an intangible one at first, but one which grows like the taste of an unusual fruit. The English exile probably remembers a landscape of green fields and tall trees and the grey square of a market town with a white-gloved policeman at the centre. The Australian exile will see a neat bungalow with a wide veranda on two sides and a bright garden with semi-tropical flowers growing half-wild. He will remember driving his old car along dusty roads with the wheat growing up to meet the sky, and the silver-pink bark of the gum trees, and the hot quiet and the white glitter of the insurance buildings in a city which stands between the sea and the plain.

I flew into Adelaide in the Douglas airliner from Melbourne, landing dead in the centre of a heat wave. The sky was as clear as a sheet of blue china, the temperature rose, and the streets began to look pale cream as the light north wind drove the dust and sand of the foothills against the buildings, through them, and away down to the gulf on the far side. However solid the city became in my mind, however protective were its high white buildings, I was always conscious of the street's end, of the wind-blown country far beyond the furthest street lamp. I had come down there from the sky and was never, during my stay, made conscious of any other means of arrival or departure.

The fashion of laughing at those who make quick visits to distant countries and then write books seems unfortunate. The unprejudiced mind and clear vision with which a traveller sets foot on alien shores will often produce the most vivid reading. Perhaps it is possible to see more on the day of arrival in a new land than in all those following. Australia, with its vast distances and clear sharp contrasts, should be described by the man who moves swiftly from state to state and coast to coast, never pausing long enough to lose the keenness of the first impression, the sweet smells, the open distance between the skylines, the remoteness of the northern sheep stations, the acidity of the Sydney accent and the atmosphere of the young white race from the north, living and working on the soil of the great south-eastern continent which had for so long been unknown and unsuspected, cut off from the history of the earth.

Armed with various papers and with about ten shillings left in my pocket, I breezed into the Adelaide agents of the Erikson Line and asked for a ship. Everyone was very polite and sympathetic, but it seemed I had just missed a three-masted barque and the next to leave was not yet half-loaded. I would have to wait for another six weeks or so. All the ships had full crews. Something would turn up, but it was a question of time. I could, of course, go up to the grain port and try my luck, but in any case I should leave my address.

"I've got ten bob left," I said. "That won't last long."

The agent frowned at his desk. "The *Viking* is due to sail in two days' time. If you'd like to go in her as a passenger it can be arranged. Your premium will cover the passage money for one hundred days and if you are longer than that, you can pay the rest at the other end."

"O.K." I said. It was a decision which I would regret during the voyage, but which seen in retrospect was wise. My complete ignorance of sailing ships of any sort was to be altered with a comprehensive baptism. As a passenger, I saw all sides of the question. I heard the opinions of the mates about the crew and vice versa. I heard the crew's mixed emotions, pride and anger, bitterness, exhilaration, jealousy and tolerance. I was able to learn, without the handicap of being too close, a great deal about the young Scandinavians who sailed the ship. I could talk to the captain about his job and talk to the sailmaker about the cut of a flying jib. I was, so to speak, independent and non-party, and that made all the difference in the world. But, of course, there were disadvantages. I was never completely at home aloft; I rarely took over the helm; I did not have the day-to-day duties and watches, the great contrast in life between an ice-cold weariness and the heaven of two hours in a wooden bunk. My memories of that trip, and the notes made at the time, are of the broad view, of immense distances and of great loneliness, of long empty weeks, of birds and fish and storm and calm, of the width of the sky and the narrowness of the deck. Against this background, there is a light tracing of human life and death, of comedy and tragedy, of the captain and his wife, the officers, the crew, and the five wayward passengers.

*   *   *

The *Viking* was the flagship of the Erikson fleet; she was painted white and had a long poop deck below which were cabins for all, sail rooms, store rooms and so on. Originally built as a Danish training ship, she was not in the same form as the other barques which had been intended purely as cargo carriers. The wheel was amidships, just forward of a small, raised platform which served as a bridge. The passengers and officers had a companion way which led up into the chart room and so out to the curve of the stern rail. The men had a second ladder which emerged near the wheel. In fine weather, they could walk direct from their cabins to the small well deck, but the door which led out that way had to be shut for most of the time.

I boarded the *Viking* two hours before she set sail for Falmouth Roads. "The motor-boat takes us out over a dead calm. The barque lies some way out; she seems immensely tall, bows on, very stately and beautiful. Her cream yards shine in the last of the sunlight. Her low white hull curves up to a long bowsprit. The ship looks large and solid, capable of rounding Cape Horn or any other cape for that matter. She is not a greyhound, but has the strength and grace of a setter bitch; she is but a shape of wood and steel, powerless and filled to the brim with grain. She has no engines, but, if a few ropes are loosed, wires hauled home and canvas stretched, she is able to move through nearly fifteen thousand miles of water and clew up off the Lizard. Once away, she must be a part of the wind and the sea and the tides. . . ."

The immediate impact of that ship on my mind had, strangely enough, little to do with the masts and yards and rigging, but sprang from the blue and white flag on the end of the spanker gaff.

My almost complete ignorance of ocean-going vessels made the mysteries of a sailing ship no greater than those of a liner, but the nationality of the vessel was important. The flag denoted a strange race and a strange language. At first sight, that was the most important thing.

The first shock on arriving at the top of the gangway was the sight of the other four passengers. There were three women and a man. I was introduced and took stock of those with whom I would have to live for the next four months. Presumably, they took stock of me.

The little dark-haired girl in a pink knitted dress turned out to be an American schoolmistress from a small Mid-West town. Her voice betrayed most of that in one blow. Within ten minutes, I learned that she was on her way round the world, and would have a lot to tell the girls, her girls, when she returned to the school. She beamed round at us all and went to explain to the silent Finnish captain that English were English, from little England, while Americans were vastly different, from the great country which had everything. After this lesson, she eyed me challengingly and her mouth shut on the final word like a trap. The captain grinned and scratched his head. I remained silent, and the challenge was rather surprisingly taken up by the other two women, one old and one not so old, who were, it appeared, very Dutch indeed. They were mother and daughter. The mother announced, with a thick accent, that they would be glad to return to Holland, for Australia had seemed indifferent to the fact that the Dutch empire was vast and rich. "But," she went on, "we 'ad a 'otel on the very shore and when we sees a Nederland ship pass we 'ang out a big orange flag and always the ships see it and salute us. So very 'omelike."

I felt uneasy and shifted my glance to the man. He was an English major, making the trip for his health. He preserved a healthy tolerance for the nationalist spirit aboard and for any inferiority complex, whether American, Dutch or Finnish. During the whole trip, he remained affable and calm, treating the ladies with a kind of frozen politeness. But from the first hour I knew there was likely to be trouble.

47

It was Miss K., the American schoolteacher, who usually set the sparks flying; she possessed some of the worst attributes of her people, all exaggerated because of our confined life. She was quite a character; she had two dresses, the pink one in which I first saw her, and a lavender one, also knitted. Her knickers, as wild windy weather permitted us to note, were to match. She had a portable typewriter with her, and on this she was tapping out a diary for "her girls." "Probably writing a book," the major said to me. "Remind me to get a copy."

Whatever her literary ambitions may have been, Miss K. was determined that if she found anything large or of new interest it should have a counterpart in the States. If that was not the case, something should be done. Unfortunately, a voyage on a four-masted barque from Australia to England via the Horn does not reflect very much of the American Way of Life, and Miss K. was often at a loss. Sometimes she grew silent, almost pensive, and her secret mental agility always resulted in a burst of physical activity. For instance, she would walk up and down the deck like a captive animal, or try to catch albatross, or give a rather alarming demonstration of how American athletes won races in the Olympic Games. On days when the sun was bright and the waves low, Miss K. would hover over the stern rail, her albatross bait trailing out in the wake. We would leave her there, her pink dress blowing, her dark hair bobbing up and down, her hands clutching the rail in hopeful excitement. Once, during the peace of an afternoon watch, a dreadful shriek reached us below, a sound like the last warning cry of a herring gull. We rushed on deck, and there was Miss K. staggering around the poop like a drunken witch, her hands tight on the line and a large albatross doing its best to haul her into the water. We went to the rescue and the albatross got away, the English, of course, being to blame. One cannot judge a nation by its female schoolteachers, but Miss K. was responsible for my realisation that the glitter of the United States was not all gold.

Mrs. Van A. and her daughter changed my ideas about Holland. The bulbs and windmills and canals were dismissed with

48

a brief smile, and the talk was of India, Dutch India, and of the great part Java and Sumatra played in the life of the Netherlands. I was informed that "every man and woman in Zoomutra know of course about our Queen and lorve her very morch. They are all so very loyal in India, our India. . . ."

Mrs. Van A. was fond of having her own way; she was the matriarch of the party, eager to tell the captain what he should do and what she would like. The only person who stood up to her was the major, whose extreme politeness was sometimes like a smack in the face. We were all friendly enough for the first two months, playing dice in the captain's cabin after dinner and idling around between the saloon and our cabins. But during the third month there were battles, and by the time we sighted the coast of Cornwall we were like a lot of rush-hour travellers on the underground, impassive, introspective and completely unemotional. So much for the passengers.

The crew, mostly Swedish-Finns from the Aaland Islands, were young and keen. There were two watches, and about ten men to each watch. Mixed with those to whom the life was complete normality were various outsiders. There was Lupy, a young Swedish student from Stockholm, whose seamanship was first class and whose water-colours were a delight. There were two Americans, one who had been sent to sea for his general good; the other was there to see that the betterment was achieved without loss of limb or life, a wet nurse, a guide, and a bit of a saint. There was a young Old Etonian who loved sailing ships from without and was now seeing them from within, and then there was Joe. Joe was only sixteen, but he equalled the Finns in seamanship and treated the life as a small part of his training for the merchant service; he was strong and gay and yet serious; he was supremely confident. He was liked and respected by all and, in his own way, raised the prestige of England to a height hitherto unknown in the fleet. Some of us may have thought he was too old for his age, but when he was washed to his death in an icy wave off Cape Horn, we all knew that he was too young to die.

The modern run of the sailing ship has been portrayed to the layman in three words: "Windjammer Grain Race." But the difference between one ship and another is immense, and they do not start at the crack of a pistol, but drift out of the Australian coastal waters between February and April, with days and weeks between them. It is the speed of the passage that matters, not the order of arrival. Occasionally, two ships leave within the same day. *Viking* sailed about thirty-six hours astern of the German training ship *Admiral Karpfanger*, and we could look on this as a race of a sort. At any rate, we had a rival with only a five-hundred-mile start on the long voyage. With luck, we might overtake her and show her sixty German cadets that they were not quite the master race they imagined. I began to study the course.

There are two ways one can round the Horn: from west to east, or from east to west. Since the prevailing wind is west, there is not much difficulty, only discomfort, in the Australia-England voyage. In old days, when vessels went from Europe to the west coast of South America, it would have been absurd for them to have used the Cape of Good Hope route, and so they had to drive their way into strong headwinds, tacking up towards the fog-bound rocks of Tierra del Fuego or down towards the icebergs of the Antarctic. From their experiences came the stories which first gave Cape Horn its evil reputation. The Cape itself hardly comes into my story, for we were well south of the land, and the waters there were no fiercer than those of the rest of the Southern Ocean. But every ship which takes the Horn route, eastward or westward, goes out into a great emptiness, into a place where giant waves pass right around the world, unfettered and with no shores to break upon. It is a vast desert of the sea, and half-way between New Zealand and South America, almost sixty degrees south, the sailing ship will be two thousand miles from the nearest land, from the nearest island, from the nearest rock. Only the albatross are there to keep her company. Only the wave crests are seen on the horizon. Usually, the wind is a gale or a half-gale and the waves sweep along with mountainous peaks and great valleys. It is cold. Even when the sun shines there is ice in the air and the spray cuts like a knife blade. Even when the wind drops, the waves lip on a huge swell and the ship staggers and the sails flap and the masts swing crazily up and down the sky. Down in the Southern Ocean we sailed across the night sea without lights, for there was no danger of unexpected meetings. Even when we were past the Horn and heading north, we were still far from the world, from the shipping routes in general use. Apart from a wandering whaling vessel, we could not expect company until up in the latitude of Rio de Janeiro, on the tropic of Capricorn.

The basic principle of sailing a square-rigged ship is not very different from any other form of sailing. The vessel has a course and its bow is kept in the required direction as long as the wind permits. If the wind is right aft, the yards are at right angles to the fore and aft line. If the wind is on the beam, the yards are hauled around to the required angle. If there is a head wind, the yards are hauled to their maximum slant and the ship is steered so that the wind just falls on the afterside of the sails. Sailing thus, it is possible to keep within six points of the intended course, and if the bow is forced two or three points further away, a tack will be necessary. That, in extreme simplification, is the method of propulsion.

We sailed from Port Victoria, Spencer's Gulf, on an evening when the sun was weary and spent and the heat of the day was rising out of the parched ground to thicken the air. The water was patched with wind. During that first night, we passed Cape Spencer and Kangaroo Island, heading south into the open sea. By the time the sun rose out of the green eastern waters, the land was only a half-seen shadow, hidden by the bright lustre of daybreak.

*   *   *

The long voyage divided itself into three distinct parts: South Pacific and lower stretches of the South Atlantic, the tropics, the North Atlantic and English Channel. The three parts are remembered by things felt and seen. For instance, I shall always associate the Cape Horn waters with immense waves and albatross, the tropics with rain and sharks, the last stretch with passing steamers. As we did not see any land between Australia and the Lizard there was no simple indication of progress. It was all a matter of temperature, birds and fish and shipping routes.

The albatross joined us as soon as we were out and away from the Gulf and heading down past the islands south of New Zealand. When the wind was blowing a gale and the sea was raging, they would fly in the slipstream and eye us with their glass-like eyes, suddenly sweeping away and swooping low over the water, only to return and take up their station once again. In the distance, they looked like large gannet, but their size was deceptive and they had a total wing-span of up to sixteen feet. If we were becalmed, they sat on the water astern and waited for any food flung over the side. They flapped about such titbits with heavy bodies, croaking and fighting and behaving, after a good meal, like overloaded aircraft. In order to take off, they ran along the surface on their flat feet, wings extended, and gradually worked up a flying speed. Landing was alarming for they came down fast, not stalling with a quick flap, but plummeting along until the last moment when they thrust out their two webbed feet to full extent and hit the water like a crazy seaplane. The birds had character; they seemed quite at home with us, even when we caught them and made them sit on deck.

Catching albatross was quite a game. We used a wooden float, about four inches square, on to which was nailed a copper triangle in which was a triangular hole. The contraption was baited with salt pork which was tied around the apex of the triangle. This bait was allowed to float astern on the end of a line and the birds swam in to see what it was all about. Eventually, one of them would peck at the pork, and if we were lucky, its hooked beak would close on the copper, and provided we kept the line taut, the apex of the triangle would remain firmly in the sharp hook of the beak. It was simple enough to haul the bird in under the counter, but it took strong arms to lift it up to the deck. Once there, all was simple, for an albatross cannot take off from dry land. It would sit and regard us with stony contempt, peering over its shoulder at anyone who approached its tail, and very often directing well-aimed droppings at our shoes.

As the superstition about the birds was known to those who had never heard of the Ancient Mariner, we did not kill the albatross, but dropped them back into the water and watched them swim over to their friends, with whom, no doubt, they had some interesting conversations on *Homo sapiens*. The only other birds seen in the Southern Ocean were stormy petrel, small and brown and constantly fluttering in the lee of a wave. Even when we were a thousand miles from land we saw them, darting from one wave to another, apparently inexhaustible.

During all those first four weeks, the giant waves came up astern and raced past. The sea put on a spectacular show. It was not always overcast, and one of the most enthralling sights in the world is that of a Cape Horn breaker coming up from the south-west, a quarter of a mile long, sixty feet high, shining white and green and blue, the crest always curling over in a glittering cockade, the valley as shadowed as evening. Under a pale sun, these waves advanced like exotic mountains; they seemed bent on our destruction. If I stood by the stern rail, my heart beat fast and then faltered. The crest rose higher and higher, grew closer and closer. I could understand why a helmsman was advised not to look over his shoulder. In fact, it took a good deal of faith in *Viking*'s buoyancy to stay there and wait until that last moment when the stern began to rise, the bow to dip, and the wave was suddenly beneath me. A split second later the bow would be rising, but not before it had been smothered in a white and furious explosion. Tilted up to the sky, I could look forward and see the bowsprit buried in the wave, a wall of water sweep along the bulwarks and burst into the well deck and the ship shake itself like a determined and strong swimmer. Exhilarating? Yes. But there was an awe attached to the days, for the weight and strength of the sea was unbelievable.

Joe and I used to sit out on the bowsprit when it was possible, saying little, just watching the ship coming towards us with its tower of white sail, the sharp bow and the long deck rising and falling. Often we were sprayed by the sea and sometimes were caught napping by a freak wave and had to jump pretty quickly for the fore stays. Joe was a fatalist about falling overboard. "Once in the sea you're finished," he said. "It isn't possible to go astern in a sailing ship. The water's at zero. And the boats are lashed down tight. Once in the sea you might as well put your arms up and go down. Better that than have your eyes pecked out by albatross. You've a long way to go down here." That all seemed sensible enough when we were discussing something completely hypothetical. But before a week was out, Joe was overboard in the cold sea. Once I had recovered from the numbing effect of the tragedy, I wondered whether he took it all calmly, the fatalist to the end.

It happened on a morning when the sun was pale through a thin mist of cloud and we were plugging along through a medium high sea at about seven knots. The wind was not strong, but the everlasting swell was there and the waves lipped the bulwarks with subdued strength. Joe was within five minutes of going off watch. It was five minutes to eight. He was, however, just completing a job, and decided to reeve the new foresail sheet through its block before going below for his breakfast. Without care, full of his usual gaiety and confidence, he slipped over the bulwarks and, hanging with one hand, bent low to pass the end of the wire to someone who waited inboard. And at that moment a freak wave slipped up from the swell and caught him around the waist and tore him away. He must, as he went aft, have heard the shrill whistles from the mate, and the raucous cries of "Man overboard! Man overboard!" In his seaboots and heavy oiled wool sweater he passed out of sight, beyond the crest of the next wave. How long? Thirty seconds? One minute? The ship was up in the wind, drifting obliquely across the waves with one half of the crew backing the mizzen rig and some tearing the ropes and lashings from the lifeboat and the rest of us just standing and looking out astern over the restless width of empty waters.

When the ship was not running, the sea was heavier, sloshing against us and making the lowering of the boat an immense feat of seamanship. They were lowered slowly, and then dropped suddenly on to the top of a wave and swept away in a brief and terrible moment of anxiety. We watched them row back, on a crest, then hidden. They seemed a tiny speck under the bare sky, one tiny boat in all that emptiness. Sometimes, as they grew distant, they were lost for minutes on end and no one spoke. And then they would reappear, climbing up one of the blue slopes, their oars like shining needles. Then, at length, they were heading back in our direction, one man leaning over the bow, the rest pulling at their oars. They returned empty-handed and the Finnish flag, for so long rolled away in the charthouse, fluttered half-way between the deck and the spanker gaff. Joe had gone for ever. At first I was unable to believe it, always waiting for the sight of his thin young figure pulling at the ropes with such easy strength. But eventually it grew to be a certainty, and I could only watch the sails reset, the yards squared, and the log begin to spin and hum as we moved away. That night I hated the sea as much as Joe had loved it. I respected it too for its constant strength, its disregard for man, for science, for progress. The sea became, that day, the only thread in life's complicated tapestry which was unalterable, bright and clear through all the wayward struggles of humanity.

*   *   *

Sometimes, on that road to the Horn, the wind freshened to gale force and the royals and topgallants came in and we staggered along under topsails, a white streak on the angry deserted greyness of those lonely waters. The hours were barely noticed as they passed. The sound of the bells was swept away by the wind. A month out. There came a day when we were rising and falling on a grey and black swell, a sky of steel overhead. We were a restless speck under that sky, between the empty circle of the horizon. There was very little wind, and the sails banged as the masts swung backward. We were, that day, off Cape Horn. Somewhere to the north, out of sight, was the great rock and Tierra del Fuego and South America.

Within a few hours, our bow would swing north, towards the warmer oceans, towards the inhabited lands. We were far south, and it would take many long days' sailing before we were clear of the region of cold west winds and came up to blue skies and a sea that was anything near flat. However, we were round the first buoy.

When we were past the latitude of the Falkland Islands, I unfolded my map of the world's shipping routes and began to hope for a sight of smoke or mast or funnel. The map showed that vessels did sail from Montevideo to Capetown, but we never saw any. Meanwhile we turned our attention to the sharks.

Surprisingly, the sharks came as far south as flew the albatross north. One bright morning we were all on deck, excited by the new look of the ocean, a silvery flatness, almost without the deep swell. I had let out my albatross bait and was idly watching it float down the wake. A pale sun gleamed down and the water below the counter seemed clear, yet full of minute particles. The wind was very light indeed and we were only just moving, sliding northward at about one knot. We were in the South Atlantic and felt we were almost home. The waters between South America and Africa had no terrors for us; they seemed like a huge lake. To all intents and purposes, they were landlocked and we were relaxing in a new security.

I looked forward to clear skies, both by day and by night. We all wanted to feel the sun again, and I was keen to see the stars, to see Orion come up, and as we climbed the world, to see Ursa Major and my own star, Lacerta. Down by the Horn, I had remembered old Captain Hugh's talk of ships and the sea, his words coming through the Cornish darkness as we stood out on the cottage lawn and gazed upward. His Magellanic Clouds were now astern, but Lacerta was somewhere over the northern horizon and our first sight of land might well be the Lizard light. I was reminded of the path I followed. Ten years of travel and ten years of practice. After that, at the age of thirty-eight, I might possibly be able to call myself a writer. It all seemed so distant. . . .

My albatross bait vanished and a jerk nearly wrenched the line from my hands. There was a swirl astern and a black fin slid through the water like a cutting knife. Shark! I hauled in the line. The bait had gone, pork and metal and wood and wire. The whole thing had been clipped off with an exact neatness. The first mate laughed. "Perhaps we can catch him," he said in his precise English. "Keep a look out for him."

During the afternoon, the sun came out with a pleasant strength and the water turned blue and we slid along through a blue and silver sparkle. The faintness of the wind made our wake a thin, dark line. The albatross dotted the water like tiny icebergs. I stayed by the stern, leaning out and watching for the enemy. At about two o'clock he arrived, a grey shadow far below the surface and then a distinct shape and then a giant fish, his tail swinging back and forth, his eyes half-hidden, his great body passing through the sea with tremendous ease. He circled below me. I could have spat on him. He nosed up towards a piece of floating bread and the tip of his upper lip broke the surface.

Five minutes later we had the shark bait out. It consisted of a wire, a ten-foot chain and a hook that looked something like a yacht's anchor. On the hook was fixed a piece of fat white salt pork. It trailed aft very slightly, about five feet below the surface. The enemy did not hold back; he came up to see what was going on. He came up from the shadowed depth with a sinister grace, not at all alarmed by the primitive hook and chain. We watched, breathless, while he circled the hook and had a preliminary sniff at the salt pork. And then he made away and we feared he had seen through our devices, but five minutes later he came along with a determined flick of his tail, sidled up to the hook, opened his mouth, and with a slight heel to one side, took the whole thing at a mouthful. It seemed too easy and too slow. The mate jumped into the air and waved his arms. The wire became taut. The shark seemed surprised; he was towed along in the wake, rigid and calm. Even when we began to haul him in, he remained unconcerned and sedate. He never lost his dignity.

The most dangerous moment in shark-catching is that when the fish first hits the deck. It is then that the strain is off the mouth and the great tail will lash out. We brought our fish alongside the well deck and, using a hand winch, hauled him into the air, clear of the water. He remained passive throughout all this. Perhaps, we thought, he was preserving his energy. Very slowly, inch by inch, we lowered him to the deck, capstan bars raised over him. He lay inert for one brief second, his body racked in a quick shudder, and then, with stunning suddenness, the bars crashed on and around his head, a great deluge of blows that forestalled any tail-lashing. He did fight, but not for long, and the carpenter plunged a long knife deep into the under belly, cutting in and downwards so that the entrails flowed out in a globular fountain.

That was the end. During the next hour, I watched the fish being dissected, bit by bit. Some wanted slices of the shining blue skin; some wanted the backbone; some wanted the head and jaws. There were many trophies there. The gall bladder spewed a liquid emerald over the white deck. My albatross bait lay embedded in the stomach. Small fish flicked their tails under the sunlight. The squares of sharkskin dried and wrinkled before being stretched. The rows of teeth glittered and became detached from the flesh as knives probed and sliced. An eye lay glazing nearby, cocked skyward in a rigid stare. Before my eyes the shark vanished little by little over the side and all that was left was a litter of bone and skin souvenirs. Quick work in the slaughterhouse.

Two days later, we saw the last of the albatross, a lone bird following against the sunrise, and eventually turning south to fly back to its windswept locale. We plunged on through keener winds, ever northward, ever towards the sun. One morning, a school of bottle-nose whales raced beside us, three hundred great black fish sliding through white waves, shining, leaping, swinging back and forth; at times they must have been doing a good twenty-five knots. About noon, they sheered off to the east and we saw their white spray trails merge into the confused lines of the distant waves.

On that voyage we saw the black whales of the South Atlantic, the rorquals of the waters around Europe and the great sperm whales of the central seas. It was the sperm whales who were most numerous; they were first seen when we had reached the edge of the tropics and were becalmed under a thinly clouded sky with a sea of milk glittering around and a fierce heat barely hidden from our arms and faces. The whales came past, one after another, in Indian file, appearing from time to time like upturned boats, clear and as black as coal on the still surface. We could hear them blowing, and one, passing beneath the bowsprit, exhaled in a raucous breath all its internal foulness so that we who were near enough were close to being sick on the spot. Often at night we heard them passing, their long wheezing breath coming out of the still darkness to startle the sleepy helmsman who was dreaming of things of the land.

And so it went on, fish and birds helping our attempts at navigation. Flying-fish were suddenly skating away from the bow like the flat stones thrown by boys. Long-tailed tropic birds were overhead, fluttering and circling like white parrots with their two long tail feathers curving and floating astern. Our tall white ship passed the Equator and slipped into the north-east trades. We were three months out, and still had seen no land, no ship. Our interests were confined to nature and the next excitement was the Sargasso Sea. Its weed, its crabs and the floating jelly-fish known to us as Portuguese men-of-war. After so long on an empty grey sea, the blue waters of the Gulf Stream were vivid. The yellow Sargasso weed lay on the clear surface like cascades of gold. We watched it pass in the distance, out of reach, and then, as we pressed north, it increased; it was always there, most patches merely a few feet across, but some trailing from wavelet to wavelet in dense bunches. I used to catch the weed with a spread of wire hooks on the end of a line, draw it inboard and bend over it where it lay, a reminder that land might be drawing close, on the matt whiteness of the poop deck. The crabs were in the weed, delicate and tiny, the size of a finger nail. They died under the hot sun, shrivelling into their shells and just fading away; they must have been mostly water.

It was in the Gulf Stream that we met the Portuguese men-of-war. They were small, white jellies with long tentacles that writhed below the surface, purple where the sun caught them. They dotted the water around us, easily visible, for they had their own method of propulsion, a kind of blown-up sail they raised out of the water and turned to the wind. In the sea, they looked attractive. On deck, they shrivelled into a confused and unpleasant mass which smelt of decay and stung if touched.

During our time out on the oceans, we came to know the wind and the sea so well that I often used to imagine that it was possible to navigate to the far ends of the earth just by taking stock of the waves and the birds, the fish and the sky. Certainly, had any of us been placed in mid-ocean in a small boat we would soon have plotted our positions within a few hundred miles. For instance, had the clouds been small and white and the winds from the north-east and the sea blue and the sun hot, then we would almost certainly have been in the north-east trades. All right. And then there would have been flying-fish as confirmation. The stars would have given us a rough check on latitude. If we steered south until the Doldrums were reached, we would know, by time of year and slant of wind, whether we were on the east or west side of the Atlantic. And so it would go on. That, perhaps, is how the first navigators found their way around the world, and to a certain extent is how the trawlermen find their fishing banks with one instinctive glance.

There was a tanker route from the southern waters of the Caribbean to the English Channel. We were on that route, to see our first ship, just twin lights far out on the horizon, moving away all the time, fading into the setting stars. But it was a ship, enough to draw all hands on deck and make minds go out across the last part of our ocean track. Next day we were almost becalmed there. To the north, a tanker passed along the horizon, outward bound, sailing solidly along the mirage of white heat. We fixed our eyes on her, silent thoughts passing in our minds. We watched her until she disappeared to the south-west. Night fell; for some reason, we felt very much alone.

*   *   *

The approach to the English Channel after a three-and-a-half-month voyage in the deep waters is like coming to a lighted street after a night's wandering on black, forsaken moors. I can remember how ship after ship went past, steering close and saluting. The *Europa* steamed by, passengers crowding one rail so that the giant liner heeled visibly. A bird flew into the rigging. A trawler gave us a bucket of fresh fish. We were eighty miles due west of the Lizard, slipping along in the summer breeze, slipping home relentlessly, but always left behind by the speeding liners. A white-hulled Strength-through-Joy liner from Germany made circles around us and a loud-speaker chanted details about our rig and our voyage.

And then, like a dream becoming reality, we looked out across the clarity of a July night and there was a light flashing in the sky, a faint shadow below the stars. Flick, flick, flick. It was a continuous beam across the lower sky, white and regular. The Lizard. Lacerta. I think I laughed as I went down to my bunk to try and sleep. The dawn was upon us before we had closed our eyes, and the water was no longer that of the oceans. The clearness was fading. There was a slight thickness about the sea, a mud-like shade in the tide which was sweeping out from the shores of England and France. There were ordinary things floating there, weed and boxes and driftwood and straw. And there was a smell on the wind, a scent of trees and flowers, of rain on rich soil, of weed on sunbaked rocks, of blowing smoke, of the sweet riot of the Cornish summer. Far away, it seemed, to the north-east, a brown shadow lay along between the sea and the sky. It was land. Our eyes ached with staring. Our white ship, wings spread to catch the morning breeze, glided slowly shorewards. As the sun rose, a wall of haze closed in and the sea grew glassy. The land vanished. The passing ships were seen suddenly, their engines sounding clear and thunderously in our ears. Half-way between Brittany and Cornwall we idled, as if all urgency was past. A new day followed the quiet night. Portland Bill. St. Catherine's Point. Beachy Head. The whole of England hid itself behind the haze of day and the shadows of night.

It was not until we were under tow and well into the Thames

estuary that details became visible. This was home, yes, England, but small things made us point and laugh. There was a horse. There was a train moving over the flat land, smoke above it, rising up towards the sun, a shadow of the smoke on the fields. There, shining and soaring, an aircraft; there, a fair-haired girl in a white summer dress, her lips as red as a knife-cut; there, a silver-grey cruiser with brasswork shining like small flames; there, a wide green field with cows grazing, crops growing out between hedges, a farm, and the smell of land and summer growing to a choking strength.

As we came up to the cranes and the docks and the busy flow of the river, I suddenly remembered the wide stretches of the sea, the intense quiet, the nights when a star shone down between the white canvas of the sails, the sense of immense loneliness and the yellow sunrise of the storm and the mellow noontide of the South Atlantic and the blood-and-fire sunset of the tropics. I had seen a little of the sea; I had experienced it in but a few moods. Was this voyaging merely a waste of time, a futile search for experience of the unusual? Would it lead to anything? Perhaps not. Definitely not. I did not intend to stay at sea for the rest of my life. And yet the taste of that voyage was so slight, so pale. It was incomplete, and I knew then that I would have to sail out again before the year was out. It would lead to nothing; it would be a vacuum in the life I was expected to lead, education running into training, training running into promotion, promotion running into success, income growing with steady security. That, roughly, was the life one had to lead according to necessities. Was nothing worth while unless it fitted into the rules, unless it lead to something?

Suddenly, I remembered Captain Hugh and my star. Of course, I had ten years, eight years to go, in the first part of my plan. This was part of my education, part of my training. I looked down the sheen of the river and my mind was free. My conscience was clear. Almost as the first mooring wire fell on to the hot stones of the quayside, I was thinking of the moving river, of the winding, sliding road that led away to the blue-still waters of the open sea.

CHAPTER FIVE

OVERTURE

The London which lay beneath the gold midday sun was cool and full of charm. There was a slight mist over St. James's Park, and the autumnal bronze of the trees was not yet tinged with the dead brown of winter. Suddenly, conscious of the fact that the sea lay ahead, I grew very fond of old landmarks. The bus rumbled down Piccadilly; the crowds streamed along the pavements; well-known names glittered above the shop windows; Eros was passed by thousands, all indifferent and busy.

I lunched in Soho, for that was a part of the old life, and I could sit at a table in the window, at ease in the sun, able to look at those who walked below in the street and those who came in for a quick meal. This was to be their daily habit, and they thought nothing of it, but for me it was a moment to linger over. It was a short distance from Greek Street to Millwall Dock, half an hour perhaps by tube and bus, but I would pass far beyond the sphere of the city, far, in fact, beyond the events of the year. Outside, the newsboys were shouting of war. Munich was just around the corner, out of sight. The scare was very real. The skies were watched with an apprehension that was far removed from the usual autumnal dread of winter clouds.

After lunch I strolled through the streets. In a matter of hours I became the greatest Anglophile, but this was only a part of the sadness that is always present where roads divide. However much one hates a place, to leave it is to kill the hate. Sentiment always prevails.

Tube to Aldgate. Bus down Commercial Road. That was the policeman's advice. It was from the top of the bus that I first saw the *Winterhude*'s masts. Abruptly, from the grey roof-tops, they rose up against the sky, black in silhouette, far above the red and blue funnels of the steamships. They were out of place there, essentially of the sea, definitely of another age. It was as if Notre Dame had suddenly sprung up in the middle of Hyde Park, but more impressive for me personally, for I was not likely to spend long in a church, whereas those masts were a part of my home; they would become as familiar as the path along which men walk to and from their work.

The ship lay out in the centre of the dock, very secure on the grey-green water. The sea was far away, the river shut out by solid dock gates. The Finnish flag was clean and gay in the afternoon sunlight, but the hull was a dirty black, streaked with the rust of time, the result of many thousands of miles of seas passing along the steel plates. But it was the masts that drew the eye. On the edge of the dock I was in their shadow and the water below was patterned with the hard reflections of shroud, stay and ratline. The jib-boom led away up into the pale blue of the sky; it seemed to reach out over the Isle of Dogs until, surely, its end was high above the Royal Standard on Buckingham Palace.

The boarding of that ship was the simplest of actions, one that has, in its physical movement and emotional stress, been the experience of millions of seamen through the ages. And yet there was a difference. For one thing, the Finnish flag was remote from the world crisis, and, too, the shape of the vessel was exceptional. The sailing ship can be beautified as a model, be made colourful as a painting or be glamourised by the nautical school of journalists, but for the average sailor she is only a ship. She might be a happy ship or a bad ship; she might be well officered or commanded by a brute. The method of propulsion is unimportant when these things are considered. In modern times, the seaman does not have to know, and is unlikely to care, whether his ship is driven through the water by reciprocating engines, turbines or by a diesel-electric affair. It is enough that the ship moves. So too the greatest worry of the square-rig sailor is the atmosphere aboard. True, he might look up at the yards to see whether the ship carries royals, double or single topgallants and so on. But the work aloft is all part of a routine that will be pleasant or unpleasant according to his tastes.

If he dislikes his shipmates, the calmest of tropic seas will be as bitter as the coldest blast off Cape Horn.

Thus the sailor will muse. But London Docks was not used to the sight of a square-rigger, and the *Winterhude* was exceptional. I went aboard with a faint arrogance, corrected by a feeling that I was climbing up the side of a dodo. So must have felt the last drivers of London horse cabs, proud but on guard, imperious before the pedestrian but careful when it came to a meeting with internal combustion.

The *Winterhude* was not a happy ship. I was able to gather that as soon as I reached the forecastle. She had had a lengthy trip from Australia and she was old and small. There was a strange atmosphere of bravado aboard. Each man battled against an obvious disillusion by smearing himself with a thick veneer of toughness. The captain stood on the poop, bowler-hatted and small, looking like a night watchman on Putney Bridge. His trousers were baggy about the knees and his eyes were blood red. I glanced around, had a swift glimpse of the distant roofs of London, and ducked into the half-darkness of the forecastle to change into dungarees. It was a final metamorphosis, the changing of my skin. When once again I reached the sunlight, I was irrevocably committed to spending many months in that small floating world. The door was closed.

*   *   *

The adaptation of a man's mind to new situations is surprisingly swift. The moment of transience is soon forgotten. So, in a matter of hours, I was able to assume the role of junior apprentice without difficulty. During these first few days it was the ship that moulded us. Later, it would be the surrounding sea, but in the calm confines of the dock we based our characters on the strange relationship between our vessel and others that lay there.

I kept a scrappy diary, pages torn from a cheap writing-pad, covered with scrawled pencilled impressions. "London River at night. It is dark, silent, and smooth-flowing, a steady stream of crude oil. The lights, green and red and white, are twinkling, moving at random; fireflies over a lake. It is a wide boulevard, this river, with brilliant fringes on either side. The white line of lights, those of a homeward-bound liner, is extinguished by cretinous heaps of chimneys. Our own masts rise up against the night sky, black, solid. The past rises over the present in a giant memorial."

I wrote that at a time when we were the only square-rigged ship in the river and we were proud. Where, however, we were proud, we were not always faithful, and whatever we said, our hearts often went down the broad river aboard some warm comfortable liner. But our thoughts were our own; we did not share them, which was perhaps a good thing for all concerned. We must all have had secret doubts and fears, but were not to indulge in an orgy of self-pity until later.

I can remember those days in that strange London with inconstant clarity, as if the box of memory is perforated. The city had revealed another face. It was not connected with the shops and theatres of the West End, or the parks and streets and churches I knew so well. It was like cutting into a piece of dry ancient skin and disclosing the startling crimson of a throbbing artery. We lived in our own world, and for us all there was the trivial and petty concern of work and play, washing dishes, painting, splicing and scrubbing; but for me the ship remained a kind of phantom, so real beneath that autumn sun, yet completely improbable when we returned to it under the smoky moonlight.

"Night watch. A good job. Idle hours, waiting for the morning, glancing eastwards rather than at the clock. I sit before the stove in the galley, for the air had lost some of its summer softness. Through the open door I can watch the slow, almost furtive, movement of ships. The bow of a ship slides from behind a building. The spritsail of a barge passes in absolute silence over the bleak backcloth. Morning at last; it is a slight paling, low down over the roof-tops. There comes an incredible and complete change both in shape and distance. Noises become associated with movement. The blanket of secrecy is cast off. . . . It is like this every morning. There is always the coldness when the sky lightens and the lights fade and there is nothing to relieve the essential greyness. Above, the masts and yards are bleak against the drab clouds. The water around, the still water of the dock, is like translucent steel. . . ."

The mornings were a source of great fascination. It was perhaps the first enjoyable sensation of a sailor's life that meant a solitary salute to the dawn. Day and night ceased to be separate, for our life overlapped them both, and dawn and dusk became moments of natural change which we noted and forgot. It was not always the same. Sometimes there was a white mist over the river, a thin vapour that lay over the whole scene. Then the ships moved more slowly and the sound of their engines was very clear. Our steel bulwarks would be wet and cold. As the sun came up, the masts and rigging would catch the first golden rays and glitter like spiders' webs on dead branches.

We were preparing for a long voyage. For a large part of the time we had to forget the sails, the tall masts and the long bowsprit. Down in the darkness of the holds, we laboured with buckets and shovels, cleaning up the black filth that was the residue of the last cargo, grain and water slushing around in the half-darkness, the hurricane lamps hissing, the smell almost intolerable, the sunshine completely remote. We longed with a feverish intensity to be away from all that, yet the evenings were full of attraction. Relieved from night watch, I was able to walk through the dock gates with the others, strolling up to the Chinese cafés, the dark streets, wine, music, and sudden, new friendships. For a few weeks the future was screened by the work of the moment. We were, like the men off the steamers, merely seamen with jobs to do, some pleasant, some not so. The furled sails were chrysalised butterflies, not yet ready for their day, shut away until the moment when they would leap forth in all their surprising beauty.

Our departure was a great relief; it was sudden. One moment we were doing our routine scrubbing and painting, making arrangements to spend a night in the West End or having rows with the dock stevedores, and in a moment of time we were slipping out through the dock gates into the breadth of the river. It was a dark night. A soft rain fell from the density of smoke-filled clouds. ". . . Movement. Barely perceptible. The rigging creeps past the shape of a warehouse we have come to know so well. The tug is ahead. The river is there, narrowed by reflections from either bank, long yellow tentacles that reach out to grasp us. We head downstream. It is a curious sensation, a silent glide with only the quiet ripple of the river under our black bow. Arc lamps shine out over the docks. As the lights become fewer, we feel the cold more; we glance back over our shoulders towards the shimmer of the city. But on either side there are only dark, deserted warehouses, desperately grim behind the falling rain."

The river broadened as we swung downstream past Gravesend and Thameshaven. It was not a time for casual sight-seeing, for there were yards of oily dangerous wires to be coiled, tricks at the wheel, last-minute adjustments to the hatches and running rigging. But the greatest feeling was one of surprise, not weariness. The *Winterhude* had suddenly changed her character. Inside the dock she had been strange. Now, moving down the river in the wake of the chubby tug, she was graceful and alive. Men who had seemed gay ornaments aboard were suddenly seen to be first-class seamen, fast-moving and alert. And the forecastle was no longer a dark place in which we changed from suits to dungarees or lay for a few hours between work and play. It assumed an atmosphere of home. We were glad to wander in there, off the cold of the deck and secure in the soft light of the oil lamp. Our bunks became personal; they were more like rooms. Behind drawn curtains we could lie and smoke and think and read. Even in that first hour, we learned to adapt ourselves to the new situation.

I went off watch at four a.m. The land on either side was flat and indistinct, only a low line above which an occasional tree rose, solitary and bare. I slept in my clothes, expecting a call for all hands as soon as we reached the open sea and cast off the tug. But this was not to be. Awake at sunrise, I was conscious of a new motion, a subtle change in the sound of the waves. A trickle of orange sun-light came in through the open port and I had to half-close my eyes against the glare. On the forecastle table there was a huge jug of steaming coffee, a loaf of bread and a plate of margarine. I climbed from my bunk and walked stiffly out on deck. The sun was shining through a pink haze. Only astern was there any sign of land, and there it was only a dark smudge. We were drifting obliquely towards the east, idling before the light winds of dawn. Up aloft, the other watch were loosing sail, and already the sun glinted on the rectangular topsails. It was a strange sight, something like watching a flower unfurl its petals. Slowly the tower of canvas rose up. The wind eddied and filled each sail. We swung towards the centre of the golden light. Our wake curved slightly; it vanished, fading, like a trail of smoke, into the grey-blue. We left no record of our passing.

*　　　　*　　　　*

Our destination was Gothenburg, fifty miles east of the Skaw. But although the world crisis was at the forefront of my mind, geographical details did not worry me unduly. The matters on which one can think when aboard a sailing ship are numerous. For instance, the helmsman watches the compass card and the direction of the ship's head. He must also keep one eye on the weather-side of the sails, for the course is controlled by the direction of the wind. This double observation is easy enough by day, and is not difficult on a clear night, but when the sky is overcast and there is no light from the stars, the man at the wheel must keep alert for the whole hour of his trick. Before him, the compass card swings, softly illuminated by a flickering paraffin lamp. From this glow, he raises his eyes towards the upper topgallant, hoping to see the sail full and steady. If he is on his course, there should be no shudder of canvas as the wind creeps around the sail's edge. But the wind might veer or back. It might not be possible to hold the course. Then, after the yards have been braced to their full extent, he can forget the compass and concentrate only on the wind.

Sailing close to the wind is easy enough, for the ship will be steady, heeling well over and carrying a great deal of rudder. But during a storm it is frightening to be at the wheel and stare upward into the black darkness, straining one's ears for the first flap of a sail, feeling the wind on the side of the cheek. Sometimes, half-asleep, cold and blind, I would arrive on the poop and be told: "Bi vinden." ("By the wind.") Almost before I had taken hold of the spokes, my predecessor would be off, stumbling down to his warm bunk. Rain would drive into my eyes, and perhaps a shower of ice-cold spray sweep up from the sea, luminous and green. After a quick glance at the compass and a tentative try at putting the ship further into the wind, I would hear the whip-crack of the jibs and the hard banging of the topgallant leeches. Then it was a question of getting her back, hard over, spinning the spokes to steady the vicious swing.

Aloft, there was a new world. One came to know the ropes and wires and ratlines. Here, there would be a weak footrest; there, the wire had stranded and would cut hands to the bone. In the darkest of nights, we knew the best ways to climb up and out over the raging sea. Automatically, distances were judged by a certain instinct, and we reached out for an unseen rope as if we were sitting in an armchair and stretching for a pipe or a light-switch. Aloft, we learned balance and surefootedness. By day with the autumn sun streaming over the silver waters of the North Sea, it was very pleasant to be astride the upper yards, swaying slightly, breathing clear pure air, looking down at the lean form of the ship sliding through the waves. Each mast, each yard, had its own peculiarities, and we knew them all. The ship was a living thing. At times we hated her, for she would always defeat us, defying our puny attempts to harness the power wind gave her. Some calm nights, when the green and red of the sidelights slashed on the bow wave and the wind hummed gently, we looked up at the sails, square shadows against the stars, and we would not have wished ourselves elsewhere. The contrasts were numerous and complete.

As a ship, and compared to all ships, the *Winterhude* was a beautiful sight at sea; she was one of the few survivors of a romantic age. As a sailing ship, and compared to all sailing ships, she was an aged freak. She carried no royals, no figurehead, no brass trimmings; she was the ugly duckling of the Erikson fleet, and as such was treated with indifference both by her owner and the men who manned the other square-riggers. She had an odd character, that of an old woman, humped and crippled, yet still retaining a shadow of former beauty. She was capricious and strong; she overpowered the personalities of her crew, shaping them all to suit her. She might be laughed at or hated, but was never loved. Those aboard, conscious of her inferiority, became defensive and aggressive when amongst her sister ships. But in spite of all this, she had a certain attraction which made us defend her. It was, perhaps, that she lacked the margin of safety that the larger barques possessed. Her masts were old; her standing rigging was frayed and stranded; her hull was thick with rust. These things made us, for some reason, assume an attitude of self-pitying arrogance. The job that was ours, to take the ship from Sweden to Australia, had the flavour of a challenge. So in her decrepitness the *Winterhude* gave us a certain glamour on which we throve.

Gothenburg, where we were to have an extremely superficial survey, was green and white, the harbour shining a calm welcome as we slipped between the rocks of the entrance. Mistakenly we thought that the large crowds, the flags on a Swedish-Amerika liner, and the circling autogiro, were in our honour, and it was not until later that we discovered that Miss Greta Garbo was in the act of leaving for Hollywood and that we were probably unnoticed in the stellar glare.

Our time in Gothenburg was one of preparation. For two weeks we lay in the shipyards at Eriksberg, on the north side of the harbour. All around there was the incessant hammering of work as steel plates were riveted into position and merchant ships, des-troyers and ferries were constructed. The weather was glorious and the blue-and-yellow Swedish flags flicked in the warm sunshine. In the evenings we would go over to the town, I to buy the London

Times and read about the crisis, the Finns to make merry in the little cafés that lay along the streets. We would amble along together, dropping in for a meal where the lights were bright and a piano and accordion made up for the weakness of our class-three beer. For a few days I was acting on orders from the British Consul, my bags packed, ready to leave for home if war broke out. But when the pact of Munich postponed the storm, I could concentrate on the practical affairs that concerned us all.

There was no real darkness there. By night, white arc lamps flooded out across the flat surface. Channel buoys flashed red and white. At dawn we watched the white hulls of the fishing boats creeping from their little dock and passing out into the grey shadows that covered the western horizon. Then, at six o'clock, we ourselves were at work. The sun rose over the trees and we were glad to get out of the dark cold forecastle and potter around the deck with our paint brushes and marlinspikes.

As far as I could see, nothing important was done to the ship during our stay at Eriksberg. There may have been a survey, but if so it was done from a considerable distance. No one important arrived aboard, and we began to be impatient, for the fine weather would soon pass and we wished to be away from the North Atlantic before the storms arose. Once we moved to a buoy, close to the southern shore, things began to speed up. We hauled the heavy sails from the 'tween-decks, heaved them aloft and sat astride the warm yards with the shackles on our belts. From that high position, we watched the busy, toy-like movement of harbour launches, ferries and rowing-boats. Below, the free watch lounged in the sunlight, the music of their rusty old gramophone rising to us as we worked. There was always bound to be a smell of coffee coming from the galley. That was the chief drink; it arrived at intervals through the day, boiling hot, strong and thick.

Our accommodation was in three parts. First, twin forecastles, one on either side of the windlass, each a narrow space containing eight bunks and a long table. Second, the deck house just abaft the foremast where lived the carpenter, cook, boilerman and third officer. Third, the poop, which housed the first and second mates, the captain and the captain's steward. Apart from a rather mysterious and definitely peculiar American, I was the only non-Scandinavian in the crew of twenty-three. But there was no language difficulty. Nearly everyone could speak English, and it was enough to be able to say "Good thing," and grin, or "Bad thing," and frown. Conversation was reduced to a simple and expressive minimum.

We were all young, our average age about twenty. Most of the men came from the Aaland Islands and had happy dispositions, but there were five or six Finns from Oulu and Tempere, all angular both of feature and mood; they were to be the flies in our ointment later on. The captain retired from the scene when we were in harbour. The new mate, inclined to wear a smart uniform and a red and white silk scarf, openly disliked us and the ship; he had served in smart training vessels and was unused to the half-crazy fatalism that ruled our days. The second mate was very young and painfully ignorant; he was not respected and was distressed if we ignored his little bleats for discipline. On the whole, it was the carpenter and the captain's steward who ran the ship, the first because of his extremely pleasant character and undeniable skill in seamanship, the second because of his command of the supplies of food and drink and his dreadfully evil personality. Where the carpenter was bright and sensible, the steward was sinister and scheming. The latter's face was heavy, frog-like; he padded up and down the deck with a silent obtrusiveness, and his sharp eyes were quick to catch us in an introspective mood. He should have been a politician, for he had all the vices of a perfect opportunist, knowing precisely what we thought and where his acid words would be welcomed. He had a hold over the captain, with whom he drank and preserved a nice balance between that side of his life and the occasions when he dropped in to see us, laden with titbits from the officer's table. At first, he was the friend of all. As the weeks passed, he was so obvious in his double dealings that we all loathed him, but he still held the key to the lazaretto and that was his trump card.

Personalities become crystallised during an ocean voyage. Generally speaking, we were in four groups. The captain and officers were there because they chose to be, perhaps because they really liked sail, or perhaps because they chose to remain in the Erikson fleet for security reasons. Finland's merchant navy was not large, and the steamers were mostly small and old, wandering up and down the Baltic and North Sea. The square-rigged ships were a major part of the Finnish mercantile world, not just aged museum pieces. The carpenter, cook and boilerman were there because they had, in those vessels, positions of indispensable importance and had become experts in their particular trades. The seamen were there because they had to do their two years in sail before they could qualify to become officers of steamships. The American and I were there because we wanted to see a little of the world from tall masts. For the Finns and Aaland Islanders, it was an essentially normal existence; they all came from poor seamen's families, and their pay and food and tobacco was all they could hope for. Perhaps, in the distant future, they saw themselves in command of one of the little Baltic steamers, a grand and respected position in a land of the sea. That, simply, was the background of the separate ways we might look on our life. The individual character of each of us became clear; it could not be hidden. But the sea corroded our sharp edges and, thankfully, was a wall against pettiness. The smallness of the world in which we were to be was always surrounded by the sea, and contrary to most ideas we did not bicker and become enemies with one another's habits. Always, the sea was between us, a common enemy or friend. There were, of course, moments of friction and unhappiness, but these were the outcome of something more than temperament; they sprang from moments of constancy of wind or calm, moments when the elements allowed us time to look at one another and, in the throes of boredom, find storm in our own lives when the sea refused to be moved.

It was a cold but glorious morning when we were towed from the green waters of that harbour and went aloft to loose the sails. One by one the gaskets were cast off and the canvas billowed down.

The jibs were hauled up and the topsails sheeted home. In the light wind we followed the small red-funnelled tug for a few miles, moving steadily over a calm sea. Then with a parting hoot and a casual wave the tug slipped the wire and swung back towards the land. We slowed. The water idled past and the wind was fitful in the sails. Alone at last, the *Winterhude* crept away from the land, almost still in the autumnal haze with a gold sun to the south and ships coming and going all around. We aloft, squaring up the rigging, felt suddenly free. Once again we were dependent on the winds, but there was a slight difference. Before, we set out to cross the North Sea. This time, our destination was South Australia, and we had before us a voyage of thirteen thousand miles, with cold winds, calms, tropical squalls, sun and moon and stars and fog. We were setting out to cross the world, our faith in the squares of canvas that formed the sails, our eyes on the green land of Sweden that was creeping back into the blue mist that lay over the eastern horizon. During the afternoon we were practically becalmed there, but at sunset the off-shore wind came out from the land and we moved forward, sliding towards the north-west beneath the glitter of the night sky.

CHAPTER SIX

'WINTERHUDE'

"A BITTER evening with a heavy sea and a clear ice-cold sky. Fair Island is on the beam, just a brown shadow through the spray haze. The sun shines gold over the great crests. A small steam trawler plunges southward, south towards the Orkneys; she is English and is bound for home. Her presence sends my spirits into my boots. . . ."

That was the beginning of my diary. After the passage between Fair Island and the Shetlands there is a gap of eighteen days. It is a gap in the written record but the memory of those days is keen, for we came silently out into the North Atlantic and struck a snarling ferocious head gale. We had no time to write, no time to change our clothes, no time to sleep heavily, no time to shave or wash or bother very much about each other. We were shadows against the sky, muffled voices in the screeching rigging, dim weary figures in the swaying light of the forecastle lamp, curses at the fighting wheel, frozen figures on the sea-swept forecastle head; we were not individuals, but a party of seamen who acted instinctively to combat the raging of the elements.

It began on the morning of 21st September. I was at the wheel when the sun came up and the ocean was revealed to be in a bad mood. A heavy swell crossed spitting waves. The sky was tinged with fire. We swayed towards the south-west with our yards braced against the backstays and the jibs like steel in their immobility. The wind was light for the first hour of that day, but the barometer began to plunge downwards and there was a look of threat above the western horizon. The crew idled about on the main deck, aware of the captain's presence on the poop and the fact that all sail was set. It would be a question of all hands before nightfall.

For me, right aft at the wheel, feet well apart and head up to the wind, it was a question of sound. With the coming of daylight, the

sound of the wind increased. Very slowly, the soft murmur became
a hum, a high whistle, a scream. The *Winterhude* leaned away and
the backstays quivered. The waves splashed aboard; they roared
away from our steel flanks with an anger of defeat. They had
perhaps come a thousand miles in the path of that wind and they
were sullen to be broken on our plates; they curled back with a
wild fury and were gone.

At fifteen minutes to six the mate sent three whistle blasts down
the deck and all hands came aft with a kind of resigned preparedness.
They had been expecting this, waiting in their oilskins, but were
unwilling to admit that this was the right moment for action. It
was too early. It was too late. There was as yet no great storm.
What water came aboard slopped over with an occasional heavy
beat. The wind was steady, but the swell was long and high and we
rolled with a jerky movement so that the staysails flicked the wire
sheets. But a red sky and a falling glass were bad omens. At the
wheel I could hear the music rise in tone. A line of spray cut across
my face like a frozen knife. They took in the flying jib, the upper
topgallants and the gaff topsail. Half an hour later the foresail was
clewed up and made fast. The wind continued to rise.

The storm was only one facet of the voyage and it cannot be
separated by paragraph or page from the rest. *Winterhude* refused
to be romanticised; she preserved little trace of her former beauty;
she rattled in her bones; she greeted the storm with a grunt and
floundered sow-like through the Atlantic troughs. We were
unable to shake off this impression of her and could not imagine
ourselves as serving a graceful ship or setting out on any great
endeavour. Whenever our ideas became too romantic the ship
touched us on the shoulder and brought us down to earth.

And so the storm lashed and roared and fought, but the little
Winterhude jerked herself into the limelight. She rolled so badly that
the ballast tanks threatened to burst. But water ballast was an advantage; we did not have to shovel and heave rock and stone into the
hold, or shovel and heave it out again when we got to Australia. The
tanks were amidships, dividing the hold into two. They kept us

stable and upright. Should they burst, we might not come back from one of the high-degree rolls. As the barometer fell, we began to think about those tanks.

I had to stay two hours at the wheel because my relief was up on the foreyard, but I was better off aft where there was a feeling of detachment. I was at least alone, and it was at such moments that life was enjoyed. The wind and the spray were not yet cold enough to pierce my oilskins. The wheel was steady under my hands. The ship was gathering speed and had almost lost her heavy gait. The sun shone through a white mist. The waves roared away and the distant crests curled and raced and shone. We were quite alone on the water and the world seemed far away. "Dear old *Winterhude*," I said, "perhaps I shall love you in the end, you fat old tin-can. Perhaps you can be forgiven for your lack of a figurehead, of royals, of a midship forecastle, of a fine line and lofty rig. Like an old senile actress, you are now bald and pathetic. But you were a lovely full-rigged ship once. You have had your day. I forgive you."

All that day we spent in the hold, putting wooden baulks in, wedging them from beam to tank tops. Every time the ship rolled we could hear the ballast water booming from side to side. We could hear it in our bunks; we could hear it on deck. Even at the storm's peak we could hear the deep notes of that water flinging itself against the thin plates, eager to become free, eager to burst out and conquer us all. Half of our trouble came from within.

Before dark the hatches were secured and the topgallant staysails were made fast. We awaited the full force of the gale with a kind of excited anger. The bare naked topgallant yards swung up and down a grey sky. Darkness slipped over the waves and our forecastle lamp swung to and fro. Water washed over the deck beneath the table. The helmsman who came off watch at midnight came in with a quick grin, shook himself like a half-drowned dog and, before he closed the door, we heard a wave hiss through the shrouds and go tearing down the deck. Shortly afterwards, the forestaysail split in two and the watch went up to make it fast. By this time the wind was howling like a mad thing and the whole ship quivered as each wave struck her. We sat in the flickering light and smoked damp cigarettes and stared down at the water sloshing past our sea-boots.

One a.m. "The door opens with a crash and a voice shouts at us. 'On deck. In upper topsails.' Even at this moment the Finns remember their pride in speaking and understanding English. We grip the edge of the table and stand like divers ready to take the plunge. The door swings on its hinges. The plates go sailing down the table and I have a quick picture of bread and meat and water swirling around in a thick mass. And then I am outside and the wind strikes me like a huge fist. The ship rolls. A wave crashes on my shoulders and I go spinning down towards the mainmast. It is completely dark. A torch flashes and a voice shouts. Someone grips my arm but is gone before I can turn my head. The wind deafens. My sou'wester goes spinning into the darkness. Now I can see the white of the waves as they roar past outside the bulkheads and I jump into the rigging. My feet are momentarily gripped by a great mass of water but I climb clear and shake my head and look about me. Other figures are climbing ahead of me. I can see their oilskins flapping and their hands, incredibly white, on the ratlines and shrouds. Looking down, the ship is just a thin shadow with a mass of white grinding on all sides. The spray is whipping high over the deck and I duck my head into my arms to save my eyes from the salty blast.

"We climb up the weather-side. The force of the gale makes the steel masts tremble and my fingers grip with stiff anger. Up over the mainyard. Someone's boot is in my face and I curse and grin all at the same time. Straining through the darkness, I try to see how many of us there are up here, how many on each yard-arm, and then I step on to the foot-rope and grasp the yard and move outward over the deck. I look down and see a mass of seething whiteness pour over the bulwarks and engulf the men who are still on deck. Some leap to the rigging. Others pick themselves up and are like disturbed ants, circling and waving their arms and looking up where we hang on and grin at their discomfort. The upper topsail yard.

79

The footrope sways out as we bend over and grasp the heavy canvas of the sail and try to heave it up beneath our stomachs. A rope end cuts my cheek and I can taste blood. I feel as if I want to sing and shout and defy this incredible wind that makes it difficult to breathe. If I turn my head towards the gale the air rushes into my throat and I can only pant and croak. A man, God knows who, is straining his voice to make us heave in time with one another. Slowly, inch by inch, we pin the folds of canvas under our ribs, between our bent bodies and the yard. And then we heave and strain and try to roll the sail up on to the yard where it can be secured."

There were five of us on that yard, five to furl an upper topsail in a gale. Training ships would have done the same job with three times our number. But we had little time to compare ourselves with anyone else that night. It took us about an hour, or was it two, or perhaps three, to furl the sail and make it fast and we hauled ourselves back to the mast and began to climb down to the deck. I felt that the weariness had been blown from my body. A wave struck me as I reached the bulwarks but I only laughed and spat salt water and turned to the next job. There was no one to give orders. No one could be heard above the thundering of the sea and the wind's shriek. It was a question of looking for a group of men, tagging on to the end of a rope or slipping and sliding along to the next mast and up aloft again, out on the swaying yard over the sea. As the ship ploughed and rolled her deck into the waves, the second mate grabbed my shoulder and flashed a torch into my face. What was he shouting? "Wheel. Two men." So that was it. I made my way to the foot of the main mast and peered across the sweep of open deck between there and the poop. The ship seemed to steady and I made a dash for it. My boots skidded; the water raced past and a thunder of sea breaking aboard preceded the great weight of water which caught me around the waist and flung me into the scuppers. Now, my oilskins were useless and I could have wept with anger, for a trick at the wheel with ice-cold water running down the inside of oilskins is no fun.

I climbed the poop ladder and reached the wheel, taking up position on the lee side, waving one arm at the figure who struggled with the spokes. We two fought together. The wind and spray were in our faces. The compass light was dim and the card swung madly. Every wave that crashed against the rudder made the wheel jerk and kick and at times we were lifted from the deck, our arms wrenched, our elbows battered. What was the course? It didn't really matter. The wind was on the beam, the compass was mad. From the poop we could see how our work had changed the shape of the ship, how the mass of canvas had dwindled and narrowed. The masts were thin and tall. Their tops crossed the wide circle of sky.

Three o'clock. Six bells. I was relieved by one of the starboard watch. In an hour's time it would be my turn to go on look-out. One hour. My legs were heavy as I made my way forward and tried to dodge the waves. My fingers were still bent around spokes of cold air. The forecastle seemed half-flooded and my books were heaped all over the wet blankets. Broken plates rattled in the corner. A sodden loaf of bread floated against my feet. Dim figures sat at the table, their heads buried on their arms; they swayed and moved with the ship; they lurched and clutched, agonised with intense weariness. I flopped on to my bunk and found a dry cigarette. For a moment, that was heaven. Heaven to be able to relax and look forward to an hour of peace. The door was shut and the jerking lamp was warm. It was comparative heaven. My eyelids were heavy, like iron. Peace . . .

And then the mainsheet parted with a sound of flapping canvas. The whole mainsail tore itself loose and we listened to its thunder, reluctant to move until the order came. A head was raised. Someone muttered. The wind was catching two thousand square feet of heavy canvas, ripping and tearing and cracking. It would be hell out on deck with the steel shackles and wires lashing through the darkness. We waited until the door burst open and the shout came. "All hands." We moved slowly. "All hands. Clew up and make fast mainsail."

Up aloft again. This time it was no small tight topsail, but a mighty mainsail, all ripped and deadly with cutting edges and fighting strength. It was dawn before we mastered her. The light came fitfully over raging waters and the clouds were black and seemed a part of the spray haze. We were alone on those waters and might have been on a star on which there was no land at all, just a great ocean. We greeted the day without enthusiasm. Beyond the ship there were giant waves with white crests, giant waves with great valleys between them on which the spume lay in frothed lines. We had little to look forward to. The galley fire had been washed out. The barometer was still dropping. Our greatest hope was to find time to lie down and smoke.

*   *   *

The storm lasted for twelve days; it blew us down to the latitude of Cape Finisterre and we sailed, one morning, out of cloud and wind and into bright sunshine and steady breezes.

The 10th November was a day of awakening. For the first time for nearly two weeks we were able to heat buckets of water in the galley and wash ourselves, to take stock of each other, to glance up at the sails and see a sudden beauty in the grace of white curves against blue. Being without wireless, newspapers and so on, we were very much our own little world. All artificial things were thrown aside. The sun gave warmth and confidence and happiness. A fair wind was the thing to wish for. Calm seas were welcomed providing there was enough wind to keep us moving. It was all so very simple. There was as much enchantment for us in those first hours of sun after the storm as one might find in a lifetime ashore.

Seamanship is not altogether a question of knots. Those who could make a beautiful Turk's head or Mathew Walker, or splice a heavy wire during a calm, had not proved magnificent during the storm. Presence of mind, calm tempers, patience, all those things, together with technical knowledge, were needed to sail the old *Winterhude* on her long voyage.

Finer weather brought us back to the old routine. The day was divided into five watches. Midnight to four; four to eight; eight to one; one to seven; seven to twelve. The morning and afternoon watches were the ones in which we worked, painting and scraping and splicing and carrying coal and water. The rest were easier, but we had our hour look-out, hour stand-by and hour at the wheel. Among my less romantic duties were washing dishes, cleaning the pig house and freshening up the forward lavatory, of which the gravitational system was sometimes faulty. If anything, the smell of the pig house was pleasanter than that of the hold, for damp black dregs of wheat have a stink that forces itself into your lungs and clings to hair and clothes.

We were heading down between Madeira and the Azores. Each day was warmer. Each mile brought us closer to the flying-fish and shark fins. We were even able to open the forecastle deadlights and ports and watch the circle of sunlight flicker on the bulkhead. The ship moved steadily, evenly. She heeled over gently to the wind and we had to switch our pillows from one end of our bunks to the other depending on the direction of the wind. The pigs were let out on deck, and much to my relief seemed to prefer to make their messes in the scuppers. At any rate, I had less to do in their wooden sty by the foremast.

Very slowly, passing few ships and seeing no land, we sailed through the sunshine towards the south. The canvas was white and stiff against a clear sky. The shadows of the sails patched the hot deck. The sea sparkled under the bow and by night the red and green sidelights sent out their colours to strike the swift curling of our bow wave.

On 14th November we saw the first flying-fish and on the following day we began to put up the old light suit of tropical sails. White clouds flecked the sky over the yards on which we worked, a sure sign of the trade winds. We idled in the light airs between the winds of the North Atlantic and the breezes that flickered from the Horse Latitudes to the doldrums. Every few hours we tacked ship. A burst or two of rain passed over the sea nearby but did not reach us. Meanwhile, the heavy sails came down and were stowed away. The patched ones went up and we looked rather like a tramp's trousers. Our skins absorbed the sun. We were red and painful and then brown. Our hair bleached. The steward issued a jar of vile bitter lime-juice to ward off scurvy.

The men in my watch were a varied crowd. There was one Dane, we called him Dansky, whose brother had been lost on the training ship *Kobenhaven*. Dansky was small and tough and amusing; he spent a great deal of time lying in his bunk trying to read my English books and playing "Dancing with tears in your eyes" on the old gramophone. There was a young Finn from Tampere, who was immensely proud of his few possessions which included a half-empty bottle of eau-de-Cologne, a scarlet comb in a leather sheath, a paper-bound Swedish novel which he read or pretended to read during the entire voyage, and a tin frame in which was a misty snap of his wife-to-be. There was a young Swedish-Finn called Issacs who began by being sad and sick and very helpless and ended up by growing into a brave tough seaman. And then there was Swimmer Erikson.

Swimmer had come aboard in Gothenburg dressed in a chocolate-brown suit, smart shoes and a white shirt with a little bow at the neck. His face was innocent and round and he was always laughing at himself or someone else. He knew nothing about the sea and cared less. He wished, it seemed, to work his way to Australia and then fade into the bush. He confided in me that he could make enough in three years in Australia to buy his little house and set himself up in business. He had nothing but the clothes he stood up in, the chocolate suit. In that he climbed up the rigging and began to find his way about.

The professionals were unkind to Erikson, whose nickname, Swimmer, was derived from a night when the watchman refused to row in for him in Gothenburg and he had to swim out to the gangway. Erikson took it all as a joke and ignored the sullen remarks that greeted his sallies at sailors and ships and everything to do with the sea. He had a bad time for the first two weeks at sea, being pushed around in the dark, confused by the storm, having to wash dishes when the ship was rolling about like a cockle and being told to do nearly all the things that would make him look foolish. He learned the hard way but he went on grinning.

The rest of my watch were moody young Finns with a readiness to jab their elbows into my stomach as we hauled on the sheets and braces. Many of us were first voyagers and my *Viking* trip gave me a certain advantage. I knew what to expect, but there were always those uncertain moments derived from fate. The influence of the steward was something new. The trivialities assumed great heights and swamped our logic. One had to stay on guard from hour to hour.

On such a voyage, days are strung together into long periods of storm or calm, cold or heat. Watches break the usual rhythm of life, day and night. Values alter. *Winterhude*'s mizzen top was badly strained and that fact took the place of worry about bank balances and so on. For all we knew, there might have been a war breaking over the lands astern, but we were too busy trimming the sails to think about international crises. The heat brought cockroaches and bed bugs out from their hiding-places behind the woodwork, and free watches were spent washing out our bunks with strong soda. So many things were left behind. We had no God but the wind, no loves but the sun, no luxury but the space of sleep, no new sensation but that brought to us from the charthouse. We had little sense of time or distance, for one tack might take us from Madeira to Brazil, one long reach to catch the northern edge of the south-east trades.

Rumours slipped through the sail shadows between poop and forecastle. We were going to stop at Madeira for whisky. The captain was ill. The chronometer had stopped. The food was short. The captain was overcharging us for tobacco. The mate was going to be discharged in Australia. The rudder was weak. We were going to New Zealand. There was a war. England was being bombed.

We passed one steamer at night. Her lights looked warm and gay. She asked our name and we watched her morse lamp flick out over the water. And then she turned away and her stern light vanished to westward. Once more we were alone.

"17th November. At five a.m. I turn out of my bunk, slip on a pair of canvas sandals and wander out under the night sky. All sail set. Instinctively I glance up at the yards and see that the wind is on the port quarter. We are doing about six knots through a calm sea. There are clouds low over the western horizon, but the sails above are black against a starlit sky. Still half-asleep, I swing up the ladder to the forecastle head and peer around for the man I am to relieve as look-out. He is there, propping himself up against the jib sheets. He turns his head and comes towards me; he peers into my face and then speaks in heavy English. 'One lighthouse on the starboard bow. I have reported.'

"'O.K.'

"'Good wind.'

"'Yes.'

"'Ah, so.' He goes down the ladder and I hear him sing out along the deck. 'Lights are bright.' I smile as the eternal pride in speaking English asserts itself again. I, on my part, make my reports in Swedish. Very complicated.

"It is a warm night. The bowsprit leads out over a sparkling sea. Above me, the forestaysail, inner and outer jibs and flying jib sing softly in the wind. Right ahead the lighthouse on Madeira is right down on the clear horizon. I watch it with a strange excitement. Land. There will be comfortable houses over there, shining cars and music. Perhaps couples will be dancing above the sea. Perhaps the eyes of some young girl will catch sight of our sails . . . perhaps not. She will not have time to notice us as we slip past in the shadows of the night.

"Six a.m. I idle on deck. This hour between look-out and my trick at the wheel is spent as stand-by. I have little to do unless there is a sail to be trimmed or a lamp to be relit. If the watch is needed and the mate blows his whistle, I will go to the forecastle and wake the men. After the yards have been trimmed and the watch have returned to their bunks, I will coil the mass of ropes back on the belaying-pins, tidy up the wire sheets and perhaps go aloft to overhaul a buntline.

"The mate passes me, binoculars in hand. He seems in a hurry and waves his hands and mutters something about land ahead. But there is the same old black cloud over the bow, the same one that has been coming slowly up for two hours. Suddenly the silence is shattered. The mate shouts to me and blows his whistle three times. I stare in disbelief. All hands? He must have gone mad. I always thought he . . . But now he is pointing and running aft. 'Land right ahead. Not cloud.'

"The men are tottering out on deck, sleepy but wide-eyed with surprise and alarm. The captain is on the poop. We are already altering course for the sails flap and the mate is letting go the braces. 'Venda. Venda. Tack ship.' We bustle around, confused, glancing at the bulk of land and abruptly conscious that it towers overhead like a great cliff. The bow swings slightly to the east. The main yards swing over with a rush. I can hear the captain bellowing through the noise of ropes running through blocks and wires clattering to the deck.

"We manage to tack all right. Silence drops. Six bells sound out from aft and I realise that I should be at the wheel. It is now very quiet on the poop. We are sailing as close to the wind as we dare, creeping along the shore. The lighthouse shines on the sails and we can see breaking waves. We make a good deal of leeway as we try to claw our way to open water. Just ahead of me, one eye on the land and the other on the compass, the captain stands motionless; he is no longer the stubby little man in the bowler hat, but a figure we all look to. If I slip from concentration on my job and have a glance at the land with a few buildings standing out in the starlight, he moves his hand as if turning an imaginary wheel. Up to the wind. Closer. Closer. . . ."

My feelings that night were a cross between the laughter of excitement and the tears of fury. Danger there may have been, but the absurdity of hitting a small island, the only land for many hundreds of miles, made us even keener to work with a will. Land seems very close in the half-light between night and day, but it looked as if we cleared the rocks by a narrow margin. When I went off watch and walked forward, the way ahead was clear. The tension was past. When we came out to look at the sun before breakfast, the island was shining over the after-rail, shining green and brown and high against the blue, cut in two by the curved edge of our spanker. Farewell Madeira. The steward says that the captain has threatened to put back and drop both the mates on the island. But the threat is an empty one. Farewell Madeira. We turn towards the bow and look forward to a slow hot passage down to the line, a timeless motion of swaying and slipping through the blue seas.

*   *   *

The north-east trades blow from Madeira to the Equator and the south-east trades blow from the Equator to a point half-way between St. Helena and the Cape. That is a simplification. In fact, the whole system moves south in the winter months and there is a belt of calms between the two winds, the doldrums. This calm belt is narrowest off the coast of Brazil, for there the south-east trades flutter almost up to the line, and do not die until they break on the shores around Pernambuco. This being the case, it is customary for the outward-bound sailing ship to steer across the centre of the Atlantic and travel an extra thousand miles in search of reliable wind rather than keep due south and become becalmed for weeks between Cape Verde and Ascension Islands. We conformed. We headed south-west.

It was not all a question of silent idle days with a breeze humming aloft and the bow cutting a still blue sea and flying-fish flickering away with a sound of a flock of birds. There was work to be done, most of it unpleasant. The hatches were opened up and we clambered down iron ladders into the dank shadows of the hold. Once again there was a discordant sound of chipping hammers, the glint of red lead, and then the sober grey paint. We hammered and heaved and sweated, sheathing the steel frames with wooden planks which would be the side against which the bags of grain would rest and which permitted the passage of air and rats. We shovelled coal from the forehold into buckets which were hauled up and shot into the coal hatch beneath the windlass. Coming up after four hours of that made us feel like retiring pit ponies. Instead of a nice green field, we saw the equally pleasant sparkle of tropic seas, the white glint of the sails and the glum resigned faces of those whose turn it was to work.

Meanwhile, the decks grew too hot for bare feet and we made rope-soled sandals with canvas toes and heels. The north-east trades began to falter. A rain squall or two fluttered past and the moist decks steamed as the sun came out. The feeling of loneliness passed after the first forty days when we were approaching the line. We ceased to hope for ships, ceased even to look for them. We were too detached from the world to feel lonely, too self-sufficient to need the sight of land to cheer us up. It was with surprise, therefore, that we came out on deck one afternoon and saw three small rocky islands on the starboard beam. I could not place them, but the carpenter, who had made the trip several times before, said that they were the St. Paul's rocks, half a day's sailing from the Equator and some five hundred miles from the Brazilian coast. Gazing across four miles of blue water at land hitherto unknown, I felt like a discoverer. Had anyone ever landed there? Did anyone live there? "Birds and crabs," the carpenter said. He had once passed close enough to be disillusioned. "Birds and crabs and insects."

On the morning of our forty-sixth day at sea we slipped very quietly from the North Atlantic to the South Atlantic. The wind held to the north-east and the sky remained clear. Water was short. The first pig was slaughtered and served up for lunch, supper, breakfast, lunch and supper until we were sick and tired of pork and blood-pudding and crackling. A school of bonito appeared, playing around the bow. We spent our free watch lying out along the bowsprit trailing hooks with white rags on them along the top of the wavelets. Several fish were caught in this way, dragged from the water and marched to the cook. They weighed about ten pounds apiece and in death were firm and iron-hard, resembling small

89

dolphin. Cooked, they looked like chicken and tasted like an extremely aged cock whose life had been spent on the seashore. But they were a change from the salt pork. They were fresh.

One night, about three hours before dawn, the wind dropped, the sails banged, and the ship slowed as if a brake had been applied. Half an hour later we were bowed beneath a heavy downpour. That was the start of the doldrums. For eight days we watched the wind indicator on the main truck chase itself around the compass, trimmed the yards to each puff, and slowly eased southward. Anyone lacking patience might have let the wind flicker and taunt and been content to drift, but the captain ranged up and down the poop like a wary jackdaw, his little eyes alert, his black moustache drooping in the rain, his braces twisted and knotted. The spare mainsail, a tiny hole cut in its centre, was hung over the water-tank inlet, a huge filler to catch every drop that swept through the rigging. Sudden sharp squalls whizzed out of the rain, making the water white and seething and pressing us over and over until the sea was lapping over the bulwarks and we were flying along like a six-metre in a strong breeze. We headed in all directions, circling and tacking, always looking for the first sign of the south-east trades.

The doldrums made us a bit fretful and intolerant. Some of us had badly poisoned arms and hands, the result of frayed and rusty wire being handled incautiously, and perhaps of two months of tinned food. But it was pleasant to feel cool rain on our bare skins, and the bed bugs kept away for a week or so.

Bed bugs. The very mention of them makes me angry even to-day. They were vile things, as large as a finger nail, light-footed and blood-sucking. As soon as I was in my bunk they would come out to attack. At first I had a torch handy and flashed it at myself and swiped if I saw anything move. But the bugs were off like a flash at the first sign of light. They seemed to anticipate my thoughts. Even when we worked in a team, one pretending to sleep and another standing by with the light, we never caught many. Infuriated and determined, I soused my bunk, blankets and clothes in the strongest soda aboard. No avail. I tried smoke. Useless. In the end I ripped out all the board lining in the bunk and went to work on the steel bulkhead with a blowlamp. That gave the bugs a shock. They kept very quiet for a fortnight, and by the time they returned we were almost out of the tropics and their time was over. My only consolation was that my blood was thin and the bugs could not have greatly enriched themselves.

There is a certain evil in a constant wind. When the sails remain untouched day after day and the log spins at the same speed and the water is covered with the same waves and the temperature remains at the same mark, then the sailing ship becomes as inanimate as a steamer and the feeling of endeavour is forgotten. One squall will break the tension. One hour's calm will make all the difference. In the light steadiness of the south-east trades, we fell apart and became the silly little individuals we were, forgetting the team, forgetting our individual virtues.

The first trouble was the development of the poisoned arms. The swellings became huge and painful. And then there was a series of minor accidents. The American fell thirty feet from the deck to the bottom of the hold; he missed the steel keelson by two feet and landed on a pile of coal dust, was shaken but unhurt. I strained the muscles of my right leg and a limp never improves temper, particularly when the day's work is heaving heavy timbers around in small spaces. My diary of those days is full of complaints. "14th December. Life seems to be a combination of pain and bed bugs and long hours of work. The blasted wind seeps up from the south-east with a kind of placid insidious determination. We came past the Brazilian Devil's Island, a penal colony four hundred miles from the mainland, just a rugged island with a sharp towering peak at one corner. Not a cheerful-looking spot to spend a ten-year sentence, but I wouldn't have minded being dropped ashore. I wish I could see or feel just one blade of grass or be in some place where I could pick up a handful of earth and let it run through my fingers. And it would be nice to be alone for half an hour. To-day we are still sliding along at about seven knots, almost wishing for a gale, praying for a sudden storm to wash away the cobwebs. . . ."

It was about this time that the steward became bored with his life in the poop, his carousals and hangovers and quick sly visits to the forecastle. He begged to spend a good part of his time with the free watch. His huge hands came out from under his stained white jacket and sometimes it was a small bottle of rum, sometimes a tart made of dried fruit and hard pastry. He gossiped about the mates, their shortcomings, their private habits, their opinions of the captain. Through the steward we became familiar with the officers, and with proverbial truth we became contemptuous. But the worst result of that man's visits was the fact that a taste of alcohol sharpened desire. The Finns began to brew a horrid sweet drink made from yeast and sugar and sultanas. After sealing it for three weeks, it was as potent as raw whisky; they sipped it in their curtained bunks. The climax came on Christmas Day.

There was nothing old-fashioned about the trouble on the *Winterhude*. It did not remind one of the great days when large and bearded men had staggered on wind-swept decks, belaying-pins in their hands, their huge voices frightening the men on the upper yards. No. Our trouble was very much that of adolescents having their first binge, and subconsciously trying to behave like their ancestors. The youthful Finns sipped their horrid concoction with the slyness of a schoolboy having an illicit cigarette. They would then sleep for an hour or two and wake up, not recovered, but half-mad. Once we had to tie a man to the capstan provided for the foresail tack. Many times men were carried from their bunks and dumped on the forecastle head to have a horizontal hour on look-out. Once or twice knives appeared, and everyone behaved as they imagined the sailing-ship sailor should behave, cursing and threatening and glowering and all the time taking great care that their nice clean singlets were not torn or stained. The captain read some sort of riot act, but clearly he was half-amused, and his pith helmet, a good many sizes too large, kept slipping over his eyes and confusing the issue.

Christmas was a strong high climax to all the foolery. We ate too much, most of the Finns drank too much. There were a good many fights, little peace or goodwill, and the third mate spent most of the afternoon sitting on the main hatch cursing his brother officers at the top of his voice. The *Winterhude* went on, almost disdaining the men who served her, slapping down the South Atlantic, through the Horse Latitudes and into the cooler, wilder weather near the Cape. By the first of the New Year, the wind was humming in the rigging and we were sweeping the seas aside, heading south-east. I used to go up on to the foredeck and watch the spray fly high above the jibs and feel happy as the great bow wave curled and flicked at the top of the bulwarks. Speed. Ten knots. Eleven. Twelve. Two hundred and seventy miles a day. On and on, down past South Africa, down to the waters of the Southern Ocean where the waves were thirty feet high and the albatross glided above the poop and stormy petrel darted in the lee of the wave crests. The days flicked past. We had visions of a record passage; we had visions of being in port in a week or ten days. The old ship shuddered and pressed on her way. The sun came out and the wake was like a great switchback of green ice. Eighty days out. Eighty-five. Ninety. And then the wind dropped with a bang. We were becalmed.

"An inconstant wind. Cool and fresh. A heavy swell coming up from the Antarctic wastes. A sail was sighted at dawn, just a distant blue square dancing on the jagged horizon. We think it is *Lawhill* or *Archibald Russell*. Certainly a four-master. The other ship is the first we have seen for nearly two months. Our eyes are fixed on her with a kind of awakening interest. Night falls. She is still there, drawing ahead, I think.

"Ninety-first day. Our friend turns out to be the *Olivebank*. Gradually our courses converge until by afternoon we are sailing side by side on a windless sea. She is a magnificent sight, not a quarter of a mile away. The swell crushed under her black bows, the great mass of sail, the long line of her deck, the steep sheer of her foredeck, it is all immense and impressive. She is eighty-one days out of Glasgow. There are some ribald remarks going on between the two captains, first by morse, then semaphore, now megaphone. There is still sufficient wind to move us both along at a steady three or four knots. The sun falls all too quickly into the haze astern and *Olivebank* creeps ahead into the shadows of night. Her stern light shines on a sea that is growing calmer every hour. That stern light has been specially lit for our benefit, for neither vessel would bother about lights so far from the steamer route. When I walk up and down the deck during my hour of look-out, I can hear *Olivebank*'s bell striking. Seven bells. Eight bells. . . ."

During the following morning, as the swell flattened and died, we tried our motor-boat engine and after a great deal of starting and stopping made it run for a fair enough length of time. The captain was going to have lunch on board *Olivebank*. By noon, both ships were completely becalmed side by side. The motor-boat was hoisted out and the captain appeared on deck, in full dress, his old blue suit, mackintosh and battered trilby hat. The mate was celebrating his temporary command by wearing his spotted silk scarf and a new peaked cap.

The scene was strange, unforgettable, and would have been a fine sight from the air or from a third vessel. Two great steel barques are rarely to be seen at sea, idle under still air, their captains exchanging abuse and invitations. Perhaps, I thought, I am taking part in a sad farewell to the age of sail, a life, a viewpoint, a whole world. Perhaps this day may be the very last on which such a thing might take place. My diary said: "To-day's atmosphere is one I am unable to describe. I feel a little sad. I know so well and see so clearly the fate of these two ships that it is like witnessing the last smile of a man who is to be condemned."

On the surface, there was gaiety and the *Winterhude* refused to be an object of pity. The motor-boat chugged away and promptly broke down. There it wallowed, helpless, about half-way between the two ships. We leaned over the side and watched the proceedings with delight, half-hoping that a wind would spring up and precipitate a crisis. While *Olivebank*'s boat was being prepared for the rescue, I made a paper megaphone and made contact with an Englishman across the water. He promised to send over some books and records.

I hurried into the forecastle to make up a return parcel. Both motor-boats, after some confusion, trundled back and forth; they brought me some tattered Penguin books and a few well-worn records. I had packed up some English dance tunes which had been played every day since leaving England and were threadbare and warped. If they became too bad we used to leave them in the sun and when they were soft iron them out under our mattresses. I was pleased to see that all the new ones were in the same state. One of them, "Tales from the Vienna Woods," had a kind of tango rhythm when played, for the needle went slowly up the hills and quickly down the slopes. The *Winterhude* waltzed her way on to Australia to this accompaniment.

On the third day of calm, our ninety-fourth at sea, the sails flapped and the boats were hoisted in, the yards trimmed and we were away. The *Olivebank* swung towards the north-east, but we kept in the west winds until we were due south of Port Lincoln and then turned ninety degrees to the left. We were by that time nearly in. There was a strange restlessness in the air, a subdued excitement. The side lights were lighted at night. The anchors were unlashed and catted. The shore-going shirts and suits appeared for drying and pressing. Ninety-five days. Ninety-six. Ninety-seven. The wind was fair and strong. We flew through the sunlight, up towards the green waters of Spencer's Gulf.

*　　　　*　　　　*

To some people, the captain of the *Queen Mary* for instance, a week at sea might seem an unusually long time. To us it was a mere flash, seven sunsets and seven dawns. Fifteen tricks at the wheel and nineteen turns on look-out, not a large number after three months' sailing. Almost before we knew it, we were staring out at a low line of yellow above a hot blue sea. The land was wavering and dim beyond a golden haze. The water became less translucent. Weed glittered on each wave.

"1st February. Dawn. A really heavenly day breaks out in a

welter of red and orange and blue. All sail set on the final lap. A strong stern wind sends us along at a good ten knots and we look ahead at the land and then glance over our shoulders, for the four-masted barque, *Archibald Russell*, is coming up astern. The race is on. Every man of us is on deck. We are all ready to spring to tack or sheet or brace. Both ships are bound for Port Lincoln. At eight a.m. we have a two-mile lead, but the four-master is slowly coming up. It is a perfect handicap, no telling which of us will drop anchor first. Sandy, rocky islands to port and starboard now. The tension is terrific. Six more miles to go. A long low streak of land appears right ahead. 'Port Lincoln is behind that,' someone says. We glance astern. We seem to be holding our own. We are rushing and tearing through the brilliant sunlight. Eyes are on the captain who intends, it seems, to hold all sail until the last moment. The water races under the keel. Now, just to the right of the neck of land, we can see the thin masts of an anchored barque. Four more miles. *Archibald Russell* is still a mile astern. The mate blows three whistles and we all move aft, eager, expectant. *Winterhude* slides into the anchorage with a rush and we have time to look at the town, a few wooden houses scattered above the yellow foreshore, and then we are past the anchored barque and are letting go halyards and sheets and hauling on downhauls. Shouts echo up and down the deck. Ropes lie everywhere. The staysails rattle down. The yards swing and move. We slow. 'Let go port anchor. Up and make fast.' As we leap into the rigging, the anchor splashes and we all take a sudden breath. We are here. We turn our heads and watch our rival sail in, ten minutes astern. . . ."

That was the picture. In the afternoon, the captain went ashore to fetch his orders and we awaited the doctor. A glassy calm fell on the waters and the haze over the land became brown under the low sun. Later, I went up to bring down the yellow quarantine flag from the main truck. It was very silent up there, silent and strange. The yards were naked, stripped of their canvas. The cable cut the surface below the bow. We lay very still. Just across the water the *Archibald Russell* swung slowly and beyond her the barque *Passat* was making sail and moving slowly in towards the land. I watched her sails appear, one by one, her anchor shine from the water, her wake curve . . . it was like seeing a coloured print in an old book, but it all moved. The ships were there all right. The sun dropped. There was a dry smell of hot earth on the motionless air. Down below, the crew sat on the hatches and stared. That was all there was left to do.

CHAPTER SEVEN

GREEN WATERS

SPENCER'S GULF cuts two hundred miles into the driest part of South Australia; its waters are pale and usually calm; its shoreline is rocky and for the most part deserted. The only large port to which steamers go for cargoes is Port Pirie. The rest are tiny settlements, relying on the sailing ships for their existence, with the occasional fisherman coming in from Adelaide in search of shark, swordfish and marlin.

The sailing-ship ports, Lincoln, Victoria, Whyalla, Wallaroo, Broughton and Germaine, were all very much the same. They were inclined to defy the kind of traveller who seeks an eternal comparison and chants: "This reminds me of Hyde Park," or "This reminds me of Clapham Junction." However, in the interests of that school, I made some notes. "If one stands at the top of the street and looks down towards the gulf, there is a wide uneven roadway, flanked with broad sidewalks and tin-roofed shacks. Beyond, a small jetty seems drawn in ink on the backcloth of pale water. Ketches ride to their anchors. A trader from the East Indies might feel at home here as long as he faces the sea. . . ." That was one view. "If one stands at the bottom of the street and looks inland, there is the same dry road, the open doors of the saloon with wide-hatted stevedores lounging around, a horse hitched to a rail, a team of six drawing a great wagon of wheat, and the shining road that runs out of the street and trails away over the shimmering flatness that stretches up to the far-away skyline. A man from America's Far West might feel at home here as long as he did not turn his head. . . ." That was the second view. In fact, of course, we did not look in one direction all the time and our impression of those places was not based on any comparison.

The whole gulf was dominated by the barques and by the ketches which carried bags of grain from the jetties to the anchorage. Only one place, Germaine, had a long enough jetty for us to lie alongside and that stretched out a mile and a quarter from the beach. It was old and rickety and had been condemned for a good number of years. Each port had a great stack of wheat just out beyond the houses, enough to fill the holds of ten or twelve large barques. First, it was usual to sail to the ballast grounds and dump most of the stone. Then a ship would creep in and lie some five miles offshore and await the first ketch. Sometimes it would be necessary to move from one port to another, depending on the grain stocks held.

Winterhude was ordered to take in the first quarter of her cargo, some sixteen thousand bags, at Port Broughton, and we sailed for that place in the evening. It was not a long voyage, perhaps a hundred miles across to the eastern side of the gulf, but the sea was glassy and we drifted in irresolute fashion towards all points of the compass. The nights were refreshing and cool and the dawns like clear water and gold. But once the sun was up the heat seemed to expand and the haze shut us in and the glare smote our eyes. It was a strange experience to slip through those almost landlocked waters and yet feel so far from the age in which we lived. Time had no meaning unless it was to do with the ripening and harvesting of crops or the prevalence of seasonal winds. Speed did not matter. The baits of civilisation were almost forgotten. Unless we had time for a quick visit to Adelaide, we were unlikely to see cars or buses or cinemas or shops until we returned to Europe. This did not worry us unduly.

We were three days crossing the gulf. On the last, the land seemed very close ahead, and in fact we were only four miles from where we should anchor. The sails were flat and lifeless. The pennant at the masthead drooped. Our shadow lay motionless on the hot water. A shark swam around the useless rudder. In the end, the motor-boat was hoisted out and sent chugging ahead, attached to us by a grass line. But the boat was a poor tug and in spite of its painful efforts, we did not reach the shallow water off Broughton until the following morning. Once the anchor dropped there, we knew that our life would change. We would be able to go ashore and wander about the street, to have all night in our bunks, to have a glass of beer and some fresh fruit and eggs and milk and meat. We would be able to read our letters with our feet dangling over the edge of the jetty and imagine our homes, little white wooden houses on the Baltic shores, modern apartments in Chicago or brick rose-covered houses at the end of green English lanes. Perhaps, for a short moment, our thoughts would be far from the dusty heat and dark mirage, and then another load of wheat would be ready and we would shake ourselves and be ready for the day's work.

"I am night-watchman again. A deep green light comes with dawn. Now, half-way between the coolness and the hard heat, my weariness slips away and I wander to the rail and stare out towards the shore. Poles stick from the water and mark the winding channel in to the jetty. The first ketch is due out at half-past five. As the sun rises, the surface of the gulf is like thick milk, then burnished gold, then blue-green silk. I make my way into the galley and put on the morning coffee!" This particular job, the making of the crew's coffee, was the one that worried me most during the entire trip. One could make a mistake at the wheel and get away with it; one could furl a sail untidily and laugh it off; one could let go the wrong rope and be excused as an ignorant Englishman, but if the coffee was undrinkable there was likely to be a frost for days. My first effort nearly caused a mutiny.

At five o'clock I woke the mate, the cook and the crew, presenting them with their jugs and cups with a certain trepidation. At half-past five the men came out into the light of the young day. I had stoked up the donkey boiler, raised the Finnish flag and tidied the deck. At six, I went off duty until sunset and, unable to sleep, watched the proceedings from the forecastle head.

The sun shone from a solid sky. Our masts, yards and rigging were clear and dark and the smoke from the little boiler funnel moved upward very slowly, creeping into the still air. The shoreline was already jerking about in the mirage, becoming broken and distorted.

Islands appeared and went to seaward and at one time it looked as if we were lying in a huge lake. It was very silent at first. We all waited and watched while the first 150-ton ketch moved out from the jetty and came down the channel, skirting the mangroves and following the line of poles. She chugged out under power and came alongside our mainyard which was cocked skyward to act as an immovable derrick. Aided by our little boiler and steam winch we loaded our own cargo, but twenty long and lanky Australian stevedores invaded the holds to stow the sacks of grain. They brought their own food, trestle tables and sleeping gear, and lived aboard while the cargo was being worked.

By half-past six the ketch's crew were lying back and taking it easy; they had been loading their little vessel since three o'clock. A rope from the end of our yard went out through a block and flicked the sacks. The hauling up began, six sacks at a time. They sailed into the air, a fine dust shaking off to the water, and were then hauled across the deck until right over the hold. It was a tricky operation, two winches grinding away, two men tightening and slacking the ropes as required. In this way the upward and transverse movements were accomplished at the same time. Down below, the stevedores received the sacks, unfastened the hitch, and gave a clear shout which meant that the rope could be sent once again down to the ketch.

That was the principle and, I suppose, it went on all day. I did not wait to see more, but as soon as the first ketch was empty, jumped down to her hot deck and went in her to view the port from close at hand. The trip ashore had its own strange fascination. We moved away, and I looked back at the *Winterhude*'s rusty hull. Streaks of red-brown almost obliterated her name. She lay very still on that bright water, the blue and white flag on the mizzen gaff drooping down the halyard. I looked back once more. And then I was suddenly glad to be away from the pigs and the lavatories and the holds and the ballast tanks and all the rest of it. The ketch swung into the marked channel. Just to our right, a long pole leaned towards the sky and I saw the sandbank beyond it, a pale

yellowness in the water. The heat burned down. The ketch's
motor rumbled away and her heavy wooden bow curved a path in
the shallows.

The skipper of that particular boat had a lean rugged face. His
eyes were half-concealed by wrinkled lids. It was a hard life, and
he showed a gaunt health from years of hard work in that rich wine
of a climate. Sometimes, he might set sail and clear off out of the gulf
to Adelaide, or go right up to Port Augusta, where the temperature
would be around 101 degrees and he would have to cover his bare
feet if he wanted to move around the deck. Sometimes, he would
be carrying wheat to the sailing ships. Sometimes, he would be
becalmed in an empty night, or riding out a cold gale from the
Antarctic. It was a life of endeavour. On this particular morning,
he lolled at the wheel, knees drawn up, a very old ·303 rifle beside
him. Every time a ray appeared on the surface, flapping and black
and immense, he would move like a flash and send a bullet singing
over the water. This business of shooting at ray was sport, not
business, for he never seemed to care whether he scored a hit or
not. Sometimes, he let fly at a shark's motionless fin and a stiff
grin would curl his hard leather lips. The rest of the crew lay on
their backs and watched the sky.

We reached the jetty at about half-past seven. Australia once more.
But the land was merely a wide stretch of flat scrub with the road
passing out and glittering like a freshwater stream as far as one could
see. It was the character of the port which attracted the eye.
Broughton was very much the wooden settlement, but it had a
green and black mangrove patch to seaward, a few green trees
among the houses, and the dryness and heat seemed for the moment
to have been banished from that particular spot. At any rate, I felt
cooler and fresher and the fierce hardness evaporated before my
eyes. Astern, the *Winterhude* was a misty shimmer in the haze, her
masts jumping up and down, her hull floating magically on a white
cloud of steam. Sometimes she vanished completely and reappeared
like a giant submarine.

The ketch skipper spat juicily by way of acknowledging my salute as I stepped on to the jetty, climbed over sacks of wheat, and walked the last few yards to that dusty sweet-smelling land.

I have often wondered what were the first actions of discoverers on setting foot in an unknown land. Some, we are told, knelt down and kissed the soil. Some planted a flag with appropriate ceremony. But those things were the required fashion, dictated by things unemotional. Inwardly those pioneers must, I feel, have had some pretty mixed thoughts. They would be glad to be off their uncomfortable wooden ships, but concerned about the native reception committee. They would be happy to see fresh fruit on the trees and fresh meat in the form of running deer, but they would have a sudden memory of their comparatively civilised homes to which they hoped to return. They would be interested in the unseen miles of country beyond the skyline, but would not venture far into the forests. Physically and mentally anchored to a distant land, they would tread the earth of the newly found continent with light steps, leaving no imprint, strongly aware of the impermanence of their presence.

That was roughly how I felt as I stepped from the wooden jetty at Port Broughton and kicked up a handful of Australian dust. When at sea I had had little thought for England. One had small appreciation of the miles covered. But now, abruptly conscious that I was off the deck and at liberty on a far-away shore, I was brought to earth with a bump. We had crossed the world. I could be no further from my home than this. I went up towards the houses with the same uneasy steps as those with which Captain Cook approached the aborigines.

Port Broughton needed little exploring. It fell within a single glance. There was the usual wooden hotel, the wide street, the painted cabins, the occasional shining stone bungalow, palm trees peering over garden walls, grape vines hanging across garden paths, heat, dust, cool shadows in the mosquito-proof rooms. Beyond, always present in my mind, always overwhelming, was the outer land with the white road leading away through space. Passing up and down the street were the nomadic stevedores and the strangely suburban residents. Instinctively, I made for the saloon bar. That was the best place to make friends.

The day progressed slowly. I arranged to have lunch at the hotel and went out to lie on the grass above the jetty. The ketches came and went. *Winterhude*'s motor-boat came in with obvious engine trouble; she spurted and then stopped, emitted a cloud of smoke and then spurted again. Children played around in the grain. There was a latent silence over the whole gulf. Far away down towards the open sea a trail of smoke splashed over the pale sky. The shadows moved relentlessly from west to east. There was, I could feel, a certain tension in the little settlement. We sailors had a reputation of being uncontrollably wild. Mothers watched their daughters and shopkeepers watched their plate-glass windows and the bartender kept his stock of glasses well back out of reach. But in that lazy heat of noontide there was only a great quiet. The men from *Winterhude* would not be ashore for another six hours.

A week later I was to know the routine of evenings ashore with the boys. Dressed in their smartest blue suits, suitable for a Sunday-school outing in Canterbury, they would wander self-consciously up the jetty and dither around like lost souls at the foot of the street. Some might buy a bag of fruit. Some might hover outside the window of the ice-cream shop, but eventually they would drift into the bar and order a glass of beer all around. There was nothing else to do. That would start things off. Two hours later the blue suits would be ruffled, the floor littered with broken glass and the Greek fruiterer defending his wife with his old rifle. Fun and frolic. Could it be that this was the traditional way sailors behaved and that it must be kept up at all costs? Perhaps. Anyway, we were shut out of the hotel and soberness found us having to sit for two hours on the jetty until the first ketch left at five a.m. Once aboard it was a question of a quick change and a shamefaced gathering on deck under the red eye of a weary mate. The day was long and the work hard and hot. The sun beat down. Every one of us must have had remorse. But no one doubted that the frolic would be repeated that same night.

Winterhude loaded a quarter of her cargo at Broughton and then set sail for Port Germaine. No one was sorry to leave. The clean air and sunshine of the upper topgallant yard was a welcome change. Broughton had its own charm, but it palled after a time. I for one was glad to be holding the spokes of the wheel again, listening to the water splashing out astern and watching the canvas curve against the sky. It was good to be at sea once more.

*   *   *

"We are alongside at Germaine, tied to the old wooden jetty which runs out a mile and a quarter from the shore. The mooring ropes are not made fast to bollards provided for the purpose, for they would soon pull out of the half-rotten wood. Instead, our ropes and wires are slung right around the jetty itself. As an additional precaution, we have dropped the starboard anchor and are all ready for the February winds which might come flicking up from the width of the Southern Ocean.

"It is still very hot, and the land soaks the clear sunlight into its parched and wrinkled skin. On the other side of the jetty lies the Swedish training ship *Abraham Rydberg*, grey-hulled and smart and rather smug. Lying out at anchor is the four-masted barque *Pommern*."

We had an interest in the *Rydberg*. She was manned by a company of forty cadets and her sails were furled without a crease, her masts painted until they shone and her decks were as white as raw pine. We went aboard to have a closer look, suddenly for some reason rather pleased with our dirty old *Winterhude*.

Aloft, on deck and below, the training ship certainly had an atmosphere of sparkle and discipline. Comparisons were out of the question, but there were certain points to be noted. The first blow was the attitude of her English apprentices who regarded us down their long thin noses as if we smelled of something unpleasant. They showed us over their vessel with a kind of defensive loftiness. "This is the very latest thing in sailing vessels, old boy." We followed them with taut meekness, while they dismissed the *Winterhude* with a wave of their white hands and smiled a patronising refusal when we asked them on board for a cup of coffee. Beneath their pride there was obviously a strain of inferiority. A hansom-cab fitted with an internal-combustion engine would not be a very wonderful car and would certainly not be a cab. The *Rydberg* was not a cargo-carrying sailing ship in the true economic sense, but she did not have the comforts and safety of a modern steamship. Her crew looked on us with only one eye; the other was fixed on themselves in silent query. We left them feeling that the *Winterhude* might be old and uncomfortable and undermanned, but at least she was the real thing and our endeavour in sailing her around the world was not helped by any up-to-date additions.

Our time in Port Germaine provided two of those strange meetings that are more common than sometimes imagined. At the head of the jetty there was a small round building in which one could buy soft drinks and ice-creams and if one felt like it put on the old gramophone and try to entice the small number of local girls down to dance. I was sitting in there one evening when a bearded Englishman off the *Pommern* wandered in from the blinding sunlight and ordered a fruit juice. We began to talk, and it turned out that we had been to the same school in England. His name was Michael. He was dark and energetic and very Irish. Overcome by the sudden feeling of comradeship which allowed us to view the whole sailing ship set-up from afar, we decided to jump the next lorry to the larger town of Port Pirie, a few miles down the coast.

Dusty and sunbaked and pretty bruised, we arrived at Port Pirie at about noon, and the first person I saw was a man with whom I had stayed in Adelaide the year before. He was up on business, he said. He would drive us down to Adelaide if we liked. His car was parked outside. It was no trouble at all. A pleasure . . .

And so we went with him and I viewed Adelaide with a new pair of eyes. The old Thistle Hotel was still there with its fat owner eating plums and custard in the fan-cooled dining-room. The flowers in the park were as red and unnatural as ever. The trams still came off the lines from time to time. But the difference was immense. A year ago I had walked there in a grey suit and flown in on the daily airliner. Now, I strolled along in dungarees and sandals and would probably return to the coast on the back of a fruit lorry. If anything, I preferred my new eyes. One could see over the top of the walls of convention.

Michael suggested that I transferred to *Pommern* for the voyage home. My loyalty to *Winterhude* was strong and I had a sneaking desire to stick to the slight glamour that surrounded those who made up her crew. This was the old bravado on its feet again. Forgotten were the sleepless days, the dark sea-washed forecastle, the strained mizzen top and the Christmas troubles. We were in port. Our stories made us feel good. To hell with comfort and orderliness. We were off the *Winterhude*. That meant something.

But when we returned to the little port between the flat water and the featureless land, I began to think differently. *Pommern* was almost ready to sail. *Winterhude* would be another month or two in those dusty airs and I had seen enough of the gulf to last for some time. The lorry dropped us on the sandy road and we walked through the scrub down to where the boats sagged at their painters and the ketches idled and the barques were tall and stately out at the far end of the jetty. *Rydberg* had gone. *Pommern* looked low in the water, lean, black and fast. *Winterhude* had a list to starboard and her three masts looked stubby. She did not present a very wonderful picture. We sat down on the sacks of grain and twiddled our bare toes in the warm wheat. The water, visible through the planks, was a jade green. A shark slipped silently just beneath the surface. We threw stones at it, but it did not seem to mind. At that time our hatred for sharks was very deep. The barque *Penang* had lost two of her crew when her boat overturned after a dance and its occupants were flung into the water. Next morning a shark was seen to break surface in the area, a man's body in its jaws. A motor-boat raced to the scene and the dead body of the ship's carpenter was recovered. The second man was never seen again.

Michael took me aboard *Pommern* and I found the square white forecastle very clean and bright with a polished ashtray on the centre of the table and bunk curtains of varied colours gay in the sunlight. It all looked very wonderful, and for a brief moment I remembered our black quarters on *Winterhude* with the food slopping about in the water and the rats slinking across the table and the bed bugs sucking at my bloodstream. There was nothing glamorous about that memory.

That afternoon, it was 23rd February, 1939, I signed off *Winterhude* and signed on *Pommern*. We had not yet finished with the gulf ports and there was one more thing I had to do. Swimmer Erikson, his chocolate suit brushed and pressed to hide the wear, was all ready to make a break on to the Australian shore. "If I can get to a farm," he said, "I shall be all right."

I found a lorry going north and certain arrangements were made. At a rendezvous, Erikson and the lorry met and merged. I watched the tail light vanish over the uneven roads and wondered how he would fare. The land was broad; it was rich for those who worked hard. But there was something immense in the great stretch of silent waste with that lorry growing more and more distant and a small figure hidden in the back, gazing out at the road, holding a small suitcase in which were a few clothes, about five pounds and a letter written in English. Erikson had a star somewhere above and it gave him courage. He grinned confidently to the end.

It was at one o'clock on 28th February that the tug arrived to tow us out from the jetty. The day was very hot, but the night had been windy and dark and we had been lying over at an angle from the jetty and listening to the creaking timbers. Dawn brought the usual green calm, and by noon the mirage was around us again, white and thick, and the black of the shark fins showed up from afar.

Twenty-eighth. Two p.m. Made sail. Starboard watch. Coiled wire and carried coal to the donkey boiler. There is a fickle wind, but we are creeping slowly out from the land. *Winterhude* is visible for an hour and a half, slowly dropping into the haze, becoming three disembodied masts which then break up and are thin sticks, wavering and diffuse. At half-past six we drop anchor owing to light head-winds. Lie very still under a starlit sky. I manage to get three hours' sleep and then at midnight the wind backs and we are making sail.

"From the mizzen rig the picture is unforgettable. *Pommern* lies below. I seem far away on a star, gazing down at a hurry and flurry between dark sheets of water. The wind is a fairy touch on my arms. I loose the topgallant and pause for a moment to look out over the gulf. Whyalla is a twinkle of lights on the starboard beam. From below comes a sudden heavy rumble and a red glare sweeps up from the little funnel of the boiler. They are hoisting the anchor. High above them I swing through the rigging and climb down to the topsailyard. Another sail to be loosed. The canvas drops away and already the topgallant is being sheeted home. I am up there for three hours loosing and overhauling buntlines and dawdling on my aerial perch. . . ."

For two days and two nights we lived an erratic and unsettled life, tacking down the gulf towards Port Victoria. The fourth mast meant that I had to learn my ropes all over again, but *Pommern* differed little from *Winterhude* and I was soon at home. Michael and I, another Englishman and a New Zealander made up the British contingent. On the whole, the *Pommern* Finns were older, more mature; they were better seamen and as such demanded a higher efficiency and cleanliness from themselves and each other. My diary records a smoother life. We came in to the anchorage at Port Victoria on the night of 2nd March, sliding along in the white moonlight, completely silent, without a shout or an order. We passed the slim unreal silhouettes of four other barques and swung to the wind. The anchor splashed; the sails were clewed up. It was as simple as that.

A week passed. We were ready to leave, but the last ketch did not finally slip away until the evening of the 16th. Then hatches were battened down and a little steamer came alongside with coal, potatoes and fresh water. Once the stores were aboard, it was only a matter of time before we were off to Cape Horn and to England.

And so once again the winds brought me twelve thousand miles to my own land. Once again there were storms and calms and shark and albatross. The road by this time had become familiar; it weaved across the shoulder of the world and led to the distant white flicker of the Lizard lighthouse. And it led to war.

CHAPTER EIGHT

HOSTILITIES ONLY

IT is a good long jump from the wayward days on a sailing ship to the fixed routine of a naval training machine. I soon discovered that there were very many ways of crossing the sea and as many reasons for doing so. The passive dangers of the elements, ice-rocks, squalls and fog, all enemies without evil intent, were suddenly replaced by shell and mine and torpedo. The endeavour was the same; the team-work survived. Pride in success was greater. What then was the source of the frustration which spread over the trainee?

The road was well planned. We disembarked from a train and were met by a naval lorry which took us to a half-built camp at Fareham outside which we were photographed for the daily papers. Uniforms were stacked neatly on the iron beds. The wooden hut in which we were to live was heated and connected to stone-floored washing places by a long passage. We ate in a huge hut; we ate mass-produced food which might have been a lot worse. We paraded at intervals throughout the day, were given lectures full of historical titbits about the Navy and jumped up and down in the gym. We learned how to carry rifles in many positions and marched through the town just to show the inhabitants that the Navy was doing its bit. We went to church on Sunday, unless excused by the doctor, and were told that one end of a ship was called the bow and the other the stern. This news excited me. I felt at last that we were getting nearer the sea.

The man who had the bed next to mine had never seen the sea and was a bit vague about the exact positions of France and Germany in relation to Wigan. Two beds beyond him was a pink and white young sailor who had before the war been travelling all over the world trying to sell a well-known type of British scent and soap. Beyond him there was a clerk. We all ignored the past and met the same problems. We all found the parade in light gym clothes a bit cold, for the ground was covered with snow and a chill wind came down from around Siberia. We all found it difficult to hold our ice-cold rifles. Most of us were confused about the details of paravanes and mines. Many of us were in deep waters when it came to answering questions about fleet orders.

Looking back, I think that our frustration arose from the unrealistic aspects of the course. No doubt everything we learned was vitally necessary to the embryo bluejacket, but the instructors seemed to have a horror of war conditions, of fluidity and make-do, of things expedient and things resulting from quick decisions. No examples of wartime needs were mentioned, and we, so often told that we were only there for the "present emergency," were given the same lessons, if diluted, as were given to the regulars. For instance, we had to know how to rig an awning over the quarter-deck, and the instructor would wander away into nostalgic memories of a dance given aboard a cruiser anchored off some Chinese port in 1935. We were given the theory of sailing small boats and were told how H.M.S. *A——* had beaten H.M.S. *B——* in the fleet regatta in 1936. There was a mention of peacetime drill and smartness, of how Commander C., wealthy and efficient, had painted his destroyer with pale grey enamel, bought with his own money. It would have been most impertinent to ask whether our petty-officer instructors were all men who had retired before the war and had only their memories from which to draw inspiration. But it would have been an expected answer.

Blue figures, our collars flapping in the wind, we were pretty content as we marched about over the snowbound land. Impatience smouldered beneath a calm and carefree surface. Bit by bit the monastic life, with its discipline reaching well into our most secret moments, became a part of us. It was the month of the first Narvik battles and our uniform was a good one. If only we could get to Norway . . . but there was another course at Chatham, gunnery and more drill. Then, we were told, if we were up for commissions we would probably be sent to an old battleship, one which would be unlikely to go to sea. Apparently sea warfare was not considered good training for wartime officers.

*　　　*　　　*

I shall always remember my first arrival at Scapa Flow. At that time, April 1940, films were coming out displaying the Orkneys as highly secret islands where German spies landed from submarines and civilians were forbidden. Scapa Flow; it had a legendary enchantment; it was the pivot on which the whole war seemed to swing. For me personally it was a group of low islands across a seething tide rip, the mast of boom-defence vessels neat and black on the grey backcloth and the everlasting Sunderland droning overhead. It was a cold bleak evening. Spray swept over the little steamer into which many of us were crowded. But the discomfort was a welcome change from barrack life which was simple squalor. Discomfort at sea was always vaguely refreshing; it made our hearts beat faster and swept some of the disillusion away to leeward.

I had been two months in the Navy by that time, and had not yet set foot aboard ship. Now, as we passed through the boom and sailed over the calmer waters of the anchorage, it seemed as if a whole lifetime of waiting was at an end. There it lay, the Home Fleet. There were ships we had been reading about in the abrupt Admiralty communiqués. Yet there was, over the steel-grey scene between the mist and the hills, a peaceful atmosphere. Everything was so still. Everything was enwrapped in a great silence. One's eye automatically looked for ships steaming in from action or steaming out towards it, but the immobility of that fleet was massive.

Ten minutes later we set foot on the Orkneys and stood on Lyness pier with our bags and hammocks, all staring out over the water, our coat collars high round our ears and our eyes flickering over the ship silhouettes. I knew that I was bound for the cruiser *Southampton*, but had only a vague idea of her shape and size. We, the new boys, peered ahead as if to see through the curtain of secrecy that covered the naval scene. Those returning from leave lolled about and observed their ships with benevolence. This business of standing on a windswept pier waiting for a boat, cut off by a narrow strip of water from hot bath or meal or warm hammock, was one we were all to know so well, one that made every ship seem like home. Our greatest wish was to be in the comparative comfort of a lighted mess-deck, war or no war.

The ship-to-shore service for ratings in the fleet was carried out with the help of a number of motor drifters. These vessels lay alongside the pier and were allocated to ships for such purposes as leave parties, stores and so on. The decks of the drifters were always covered with spray and shelterless, but they bore us to our first fighting ships and that gave them a certain virtue.

Our party, about a hundred and fifty, left Lyness pier as the sun was dropping away behind the mist and the steel of the water was turning to gunmetal. The bluff bow carved its way through the shadows and tiny lights glimmered. A searchlight was suddenly flung up horizontally into the moist air. Through the stillness came the sudden music of bells. Six o'clock. Thin traces of smoke trailed from the compact line of berthed destroyers. A signal lamp flickered with immense speed from the masthead of the flagship. We passed the glowing circles of lighted ports and looked up at the occasional figure who leaned from a rail and watched us go. As dusk deepened, the ship receded from sight and a great emptiness fell over the Flow like a cold shroud. Lights were blacked out and we were very much alone there, just a group of red cigarette ends and the white wash of the bow wave.

War, I suppose, is essentially anti-climactic. The whole business of modern victory seems to defeat its object. My first night with the Fleet fell within this observation. The *Southampton* was at sea, God knew where. The cruiser squadron was at sea. We were dumped aboard the *Dunluce Castle*, a weary old liner, grey-painted and listing, surrounded by lighters and drifters and oil and floating cabbages. The gangway was pretty well painted to the hull, for she had not moved for a good while. Despairing disgruntled petty

officers met us without enthusiasm. Their voices came out of the
darkness like grit in the wind. "Get along there. Mess 40 and God
help you. Get along. Make it snappy. What the hell do you think
this is? A pleasure liner?"

Mess 40. God didn't help an awful lot. There was one table
which, at full capacity, might seat thirty men for a meal and was
now trying to cope with one hundred and twenty. There were
fifteen plates and eight cups between the lot of us. Knives and forks
were dimly remembered by those who had been there for over a
week. Men lay about in the corners. Those with hammocks had
to stay in them all the time for fear of losing their advantage. They
were fed by hand on slices of bread and bits of bacon and if a cup
ever came their way, on the sticky sweet naval tea. We gazed
around despondently and remembered with nostalgia the kinder-
garten at Fareham when we had lined up neatly for full plates and
marched to our appointed places. The loudspeaker blared a list
of ships and names. Some faces brightened; some fell. As each
vessel returned from sea her name was broadcast and men drafted
to her were off and away. They must have felt like reprieved
murderers.

This was war, and we did not really complain. The Norwegian
operations had kept the Fleet at sea for such long periods at a time
that the accommodation ship was bursting her sides with new
arrivals. It could not be helped. A feeling of resigned martyrdom
came to our rescue and we laughed at ourselves and the world. That
was for the first two days.

By the end of a week our smiles were considerably thinner, and I
daresay our faces were too. Added to that, our nerves were just
beneath the skin. Each time the loudspeaker was switched on we
listened for our names. Each time we found a way of stepping over
sleeping forms and reaching the deck, we saw a dim shape enter the
Flow and raced back in case it was our cruiser. But movement was
restricted. It was not good policy to desert one's claim for long.
A strip of deck, six feet by two feet, was worth a good bit. If one
had a strip it meant that sleep was possible. If the strip was away in

a shadowed corner, it meant that sleep was probable. The hammock owners could have done a brisk business had they been sufficiently energetic.

The *Southampton* did not come. Ten days passed. Two weeks. And then, one morning, just as I was becoming rather glamorous as the oldest inhabitant and head of the lost souls, I was told to get my gear and board the next boat for the destroyer *Volunteer*. My ship was remaining in Norway. She would not come for me, so I would have to go to her. I grinned. The night was pitch dark and the Fleet was under warning of imminent air attack. Red warning. Guns pointed skyward. The silence was broken only by the scraping of boots on steel decks. It was a night of sudden movement and tense excitement. The *Volunteer* was old and of unfortunate design, but she looked like a streak of black fury as she lay against the misty darkness of the islands. Her deck as I stepped aboard seemed to quiver with restrained power. I glanced around. Depth charges were in place. The guns were manned. A deep throbbing came from somewhere inside the hull. At last I felt the chains which had for so long tethered me to Fareham and Chatham, to drills and routines and inspections, were broken.

We left for Norway at dawn. I stood on the cold deck as we moved with an almost incredible swiftness across the Flow and out into the white tide of the Pentland Firth. There was no ceremony, no salute. We just slipped out of the boom and headed towards the lemon-yellow sunrise with the islands dark and flat astern and the masts of the battleships sinking down into the skyline. A north wind whipped spray high over the funnel and the main deck was like a long shadow on the sea. For the *Volunteer* this was a return to the fjord war, but for me it was the baptism and the jump off the spring-board's end.

The North Sea was a sheet of polished silver. Somewhere, and according to some plan, we came up with a large fleet tanker escorted by another destroyer. After that, the three ships steamed north-eastward, through one night and into a second dawn of white glitter and washed-out chrome. The air grew colder. Below, in the narrow mess-decks with the hammocks swinging above our heads and their shadows crossing the steel curve of the vessel's flanks, we prepared our meals and read our books and smoked home-made cigarettes. Once or twice, friendly aircraft appeared from the clouds, dropped red and green flares and vanished. It all seemed too easy, this war, too matter-of-fact. This was before the collapse at Sedan, and before the rest of the setbacks. We took our voyage as a matter of course in those April days of 1940. Within a month we were to be shaken, and within two months we would be out of Norway, out of Belgium and ready to clear out of France. But for the moment, if the staff made a plan it was carried out. The particular plan with which we were concerned was to escort a tanker to a deep and narrow fjord in which the Fleet could be fuelled without danger. All would be well if we were not sighted from the air, and as if keeping to a complicated staff schedule, a blizzard came out of the north-east and the snowflakes were like a whispering white curtain, impenetrable to German aviators, even if they managed to lift their heavy machines off the Stavanger airstrip. And so we were back at the old game of seamanship, slipping through the blowing snow and drawing closer and closer to the rocks of Norway. Navigation was more important than gunnery. The sky was mud grey with the sea dark-lipped and the lean shape of the destroyer the only solid thing there. Sometimes we caught a glimpse of the other ships, and once or twice their signal lamps came out of the whiteness like probing sword blades. Night was only a draining away of the light, a thickening of the storm, a time when only the closest waves were seen and when stars took the sun's place far above those whirling snow-clouds.

I was a passenger there, performing no useful function and most probably a damned nuisance with eternal questions. A destroyer is small enough for each man to be recognised as one who has a certain job and is known to be good, bad or indifferent at it. No one man is so far within the confines of his own department that he is unknown to the head of the next department. I liked the atmosphere. We did not have a general mass-production of meals, but each mess prepared its own and took it along to the galley where it was cooked. Each mess had a hand responsible for buying and finding the necessities for the meals. It was a system which worked better when the ship was in a large port, near shops and markets. Off Norway, the provision room was the sole source of supply and its contents were not particularly varied.

The voyage, the crossing of the North Sea, made me realise that the life in the Navy had the same basic routines as that of the square-rigged ships. There were watches, look-out and so on. There were wet decks and cold fingers, hot cups of cocoa at frequent intervals, washing decks and dishes, chipping rust and painting, sewing on buttons and drying oilskins. The endeavour of the team was there. The difference between the two ways of life was made apparent by the abrupt decision of our asdic operator that a German U-boat was nearby. Action stations! The *Volunteer* went over like a racing yacht as she turned 150 degrees and shot off at full speed towards the south-east. The snow was thinner. We could see for about two miles, four thousand yards over dark grey unsettled water. The tanker began a rather laborious zigzag.

Within the next hour, I was conscious of a strange sensation of detachment. The business of dropping depth charges, something made familiar in the cinema, was as unreal at that moment as it had been in the Odeon, Leicester Square. The charges flew over the side and their explosions hit our steel plates. The water bubbled astern and the usual column of spray sploshed up. It was almost impossible to realise that there were about sixty Germans some three hundred feet below us and that we were trying our best to blast them from their steel shell into the killing pressure of the water. In three steps I was turned from a civilian to a combatant. Uniform made no difference, but the somersault of my frame of mind did the trick. First, there was the sensation of being part of a huge audience, apart from the play yet important from a box-office and applause angle. Second, there was the sudden shock which followed the realisation of the proximity of the enemy and the intent to kill. Thirdly, one recovered the emotional excitement of a chase, whether hunter or hunted, and the whole action became a trial of brain and science. Depth charge against torpedo. Destroyer against U-boat. In the application of cold-blooded scientific training, the human element became distant and we thought no more about the likelihood of our killing the submarine crew than the likelihood of their killing us.

We did not, as far as I know, do any vital damage to that enemy submarine. Our orders were to see the tanker safely to its destination, to guard it against attack rather than to destroy the attackers. We turned away and raced towards the east. In the late evening, when the sky was temporarily clear and the snowclad mountains were rising high above still, black water, we came to the narrow fjord which the Navy called Graveyard Creek.

*   *   *

During the last week of that cold April, the German wireless broadcast a report that the British Fleet was being refuelled from a tanker which had been hidden in one of the dark and narrow fjords. The German air force, the broadcast went on, would deal with the matter. But they did nothing of the kind. I lived on that hidden tanker for a week, watching the ships come sliding alongside after dark, taking in fuel and vanishing again before daybreak. Sooner or later, it was expected that the *Southampton* would arrive, and I was condemned to walk the steel snow-covered decks with hope sinking very low indeed.

Graveyard Creek was less final than its name suggested. To it were brought ships that had been too badly damaged to steam back across the North Sea. In the fjord, they were patched up and so far as possible made seaworthy. So long as the snow clouds blew low and fast off the mountains, they were safe. Most days, the sky was dull and leaden and against it the flakes seemed like sandy smoke. The rocky foreshore was jagged black and white. Close on either side the mountains rose up like thick curtains, solid, impregnable. We were cut off from the war there. No sight of it penetrated the screen. No sound of it drifted through the murk.

I can remember the late evening when we watched and waited for the cruiser *Arethusa* to arrive. Visibility was barely two hundred yards. A cold blustering wind was coming in from the sea and sweeping back from the face of the mountains. There were no lights. The scene was grim in the extreme, grim and desolate. Under our feet the tanker's decks were like black ice. Snow festooned the steel of the rigging and there was a patch of running water, water on warm metal, right above the rising heat of the engine room.

We stood out there in the cold, coat collars up round our ears, most of us in what were known as "comforts," balaclava helmets, gloves, scarves and heavy stockings. On such nights, we did not think very much about the source of these things, the knitting circles and so on, but we were moderately warm. A flickering, piercing blue light appeared up under the slopes at the head of the fjord. An acetylene burner. They were trying to cut a hole through the smashed bow of a destroyer so that they could get the bodies out. This was a suitable night for such work. Natural refrigeration has its advantages.

The *Arethusa* was half an hour late; she came in out of the blasted waters of the open sea, a monstrous shadow, a black and distorted mass, orders coming across to us clearly. We could hear the ring of her bridge telegraph, faint and disrupted by a sweep of wind. She came in a little too fast. Her great steel bulk edged closer and closer and then one of those fjord blusters caught her stern and her flared bow caught the tanker's upper works. Steel bent like melting butter. Wood splinters flew. High above us a dark figure cursed and swore and then a clipped order came down, calm and precise. The tanker shuddered. The cruiser went slowly astern, but the ropes were between the two ships and they were drawn in to one another with deadly slowness, inch by inch. Winches rattled. The crew of that cruiser leaned over and gazed down at us and told us something about the war. "It's going O.K," they said. "You've got a cushy number. Want some nutty? Hey, there. I think we've got some mail for you. . . ."

For another five days I watched the Navy come and go. We saw no enemy aircraft. The face of the land was empty. And then one morning a Tribal-class destroyer came alongside and I was told to board her for the short trip to Harstad, the British base on the Lofoten Islands, off which the *Southampton* was supposed to be lying.

We went northward through the thickness of a whispering blizzard, a low wind driving the flakes along the deck and over the wave crests. But when we steamed into Vestfjord and crept up to the waters of the anchorage, a warm sun was shining and slopes were a vivid green; the houses looked clean, their white-painted timbers shining out from the trees; the water was dotted with ships; after Graveyard Creek, it looked like Paradise.

Before nightfall, I was at last aboard my own ship, lost in the immensity of the gangways and messes and ladders and steel water-tight doors which had to be opened every time one went down to the bathroom or up to the hangar. The hull and upperworks were painted a chocolate and dark green, flowing camouflage that made us merge into the landscape as we lay close under the tall mountains. Inside, however, it was all white and shining, humming with fans and ventilation and power. Cruiser life was confusing, but surprisingly informal. We went about in duffle coats and wool helmets and seaboots, never off guard, never long from the second degree of readiness, known as "Defence stations."

The naval rating in a big ship is very much enclosed within departmental walls. I lived with the seamen, thought with them, laughed with them and spent time off watch playing chess and ludo with them. Signallers, stokers, telegraphists and torpedomen were creatures of another world. We knew very little of what went on, despite periodical broadcasts by the commander. News of the war came through the wireless from London, but we had little idea where Namsos was, or where the British Army were fighting. We went about our routine work and waited for the war to come to us.

The first operation in which I took part was the evacuation of Andalsnes. This whole business was to me a drawn-out period of darkness and ignorance. I saw little of what went on and was told nothing. My action station was in the 6-inch magazine far down in the stomach of the ship, a cold place where it was almost impossible to remain still for long and where lights glowed fitfully on bare steel and the blunt end of layers of shells. I was, to the ship, merely a pair of hands, useful for putting a shell in the bottom of the electric hoist in which it would rise into the turret. There was no reason at all why I should have known what we were firing at or what was firing at us. But because I was inquisitive I felt defeated by the total lack of news. Shut away in the magazine I tried to picture the scene on deck and wished myself up there in the snow and the darkness or, for all I knew, under a clear white moon.

Andalsnes went off without a hitch. There was a brief air attack, a German bomber swooping on us from the dawn behind the eastern mountain tops. I heard little of this, just a soft grunt of the 4-inch guns and the twang on the hull as a bomb hit the surface far away. But that was a baptism and I had been in action. The strange remoteness of it all made me realise how different was the Navy from the other services. There was an unemotional unity of crew, a time when seven hundred men worked as one, when success depended on the whole, not the individual. About that time I began to see the uses of uniform and square parades, the complete merging of large numbers of men into a single unit. Through a drab constancy of training, our actions in the face of danger became quite instinctive and there were times when we blessed the raw-boned petty officers who kept us at it, hour after hour, until thought was barely necessary and our hands and feet obeyed an order with a kind of reflex action.

Back at Harstad things were warming up. There was talk of a crisis. There was rumour of the capture of Narvik by our forces. And then the air attacks on the anchorage started. In fact, those waters were too deep for us to attach ourselves to the bottom, and in any case, we were always on our guard against being surprised as a sitting target. The ship would lie still, kept from touching the cliffs by a watchful officer-of-the-watch, who moved the engines dead slow from time to time. My action station had been altered to that of a loading number for the port-after 4.7 high-angled gun. This pleased me, for it meant that I was on the upper deck and could watch the proceedings myself. It was a great relief to know the extent of the danger, apart from the fact that there was a feeling of comparative safety in being out in the open air and not shut in with a lot of high-explosive shells.

"Red warning." That meant that we were in imminent danger of being attacked from the air. I must confess that before I experienced regular attacks I was keen for things to get going. Routine seemed out of place and monotonous in the May sunshine with the Norwegian foreshore looking so close, so very pleasant. One almost hoped for action. It came soon enough.

We were out of the forecastle, out under the shining barrels of the 6-inch guns, mending clothes and chatting, waiting for the bugle which would call us from the after-breakfast pause to the day's work. It was warm. The waters of the fjord sparkled. The sky over the mountains was pale and white and only tinged with colour in the east where a washed-out yellowness succeeded the brilliance of daybreak. A few Norwegian fishing boats moved from place to place, the staccato sound of their engines jerking into the stillness of the air. On one of them there was a girl with golden hair. We watched her pass with a silent stare.

"Red warning." It came suddenly. All the ships were silver and resting, and then in a flash each of them had huge red flags rising to the yard-arms and a siren sounded from one of the destroyers, an urgent string of quick blasts. Bugles were calling "Action stations." We were all running for our posts, some dropping down the hatches, others jostling on the deck, our eyes flicking skywards, towards the southern sky. My gun, P.2, was already manned, phone numbers making contact with the control, the whine of the electrical training motors in our ears. Shell lockers were flung open and I took up my position near the top of the hoist from which I would carry the shells to the gun.

And then there was a pause. Perhaps after all it was an anti-climax, one of the never-ending false alarms. But someone pointed to the west and we could see shell bursts in the sky and hear a distant echo of gunfire. On shore, a 3-inch army gun went off with its ear-splitting crack. We could see the men running up the sandy roads and a staff car came swinging down the hill from the trees. The fishing boats vanished. We began to vibrate, to move across the steel water to the wide throat of the fjord where we would have more room to manœuvre from the path of the bombs. The guns swung upward, following the directors. We all wore steel helmets and white anti-flash gloves. The red flag streamed out in the sun-light.

The captain of P.2, an experienced petty officer, was as unmoved as a lump of granite, crisp in his orders. We were tightly closed up, rigid at our posts. The movement of the guns went on almost automatically, pointers being followed. When the time came to open fire, few of the gun's crew would have time or chance to look at the target. A brief interval after the warning bell, the guns would be fired electrically from the bridge.

Six enemy aircraft came over that morning; they were flying high, just silver glints against the misty blue of the sky. All heads were well back, and the R.A.F. man, who had something to do with our two Walrus flying boats and was also a loading number, tapped with the ends of his fingers on the wooden rail of the shell lockers. A young sub-lieutenant was standing on the top of the motor launch, scanning the sky with a pair of binoculars. Somewhere to our left a destroyer's siren wailed and her guns barked. Far above I could see the long-tailed aircraft and the bursts of smoke in her path. And then our guns were opening fire and I was dashing from hoist to locker and from hoist to gun. The ship turned under full helm and there was a moment when the sun was turning in the sky and the enemy machine was heading straight at us. I could see the bombs, but their noise was faint under the gun roar. The fine light whistle came to us all. And then the bombs passed over the fore-mast, small, white and shining. They vanished behind the bow and must have the hit the water a hundred yards ahead of us. Incendiaries? The guns swung; the next plane was coming in. We had lost sight of the little houses and the trees and the army men on the hillside; we had lost sight of the fishing boats and forgotten the blonde. All our attention was focused on the steel barrels of the guns, on the brass shell-cases which piled on the deck, on the high blue-white of the sky. When the raid came to an end we leaned back against the nearest support and wiped our foreheads and lit cigarettes. The bugle blared out the All Clear and the ensuing silence was one of complete peace.

Every morning, with sustained regularity, the Germans sent over four or five or six high-flying bombers. They kept us busy and made us jumpy. One note of the bugle was enough to send us running, dropping what we were doing and grabbing our helmets as we went. At night I used to lie in my hammock and feel the dry and heavy ache in my stomach which became a part of me. It was a physical reaction about which I could do nothing. It was a part of the knowledge of the certainty of a morning raid. There was so little doubt about the time and strength of the attack that excitement could not help. Day after day we spent the forenoons firing away with desperation. We were never hit, but a salvo crossed us and one bomb, landing close alongside, deluged us with water and sent its splinters into hull and gun shield and bridge. Our starboard side was like a pepperpot. The captain was hit in the leg and was taken off to the hospital ship. The raids went on.

All this was a very small facet of the Norwegian war, and we were isolated there, chosen as anti-aircraft guardship for the base. Our accuracy was improving and so was the rate of fire. We claimed to be the best A.A. ship in the Home Fleet and had enough practice to achieve a distinction. The 6-inch guns crews were sucking their teeth and wondering if they would ever get a chance to use their weapons. They had to wait until we went down to act as floating artillery in the army's final attempt to capture the port of Narvik.

*　　　*　　　*

For some time it had been obvious that there was an operation of importance on the staff agenda. Secrecy was maintained, but certain preparations were made which let the cat out of the bag. For instance, piles of 6-inch shells were hoisted on deck and re-fused. Their round conical time-fuses were put away and they were fitted with dangerous-looking direct-impact noses, black shining bell-pushes protruding from the brass. We on the 4.7's were given practice runs against the ship's motor-boats which were supposed to be E-boats. Another cruiser arrived. Landing parties were detailed, drawn up on the flight deck and drilled in full equipment. Yes. It was obvious that something was about to happen.

On the evening before we left for Narvik the commander made one of his famous broadcasts, detailing the forthcoming action. It was a pep talk, but it gave us enough information to keep us quiet. Rumours ceased flowing from mess to mess; signallers lost some of their secretive know-all glamour; the presence of mysterious French and Polish officers in the wardroom was explained.

As planned, our part in the show sounded immensely simple. Narvik lies at the head of a long fjord, the town lying back in an inlet which is protected in the west by a low scrub-covered hill and to the east by the rising cliffs of the granite mountain-sides. It seemed that the British held the summit of the low western hill, but were unable to advance down it because the Germans had gun positions high up on the mountain slopes and raked the opposite side with constant fire of machine-guns and 20-mms. Our job was to shell the German positions and cover the British attack. With the allied forces there was a group of French Legionaires, a detachment of Polish artillery and some Norwegian infantry. Air power was almost completely held by the enemy. As I remember it, zero hour was midnight, but the lightness of those pale northern nights was more or less timeless, and the hour was meaningless except for purposes of synchronisation.

In order to stimulate the element of surprise, we took a short cut down from the base to the dark still waters of the upper reaches of the Vestfjord. One cruiser at least had suffered from the presence

of uncharted rocks in these narrow channels, and we went carefully
but fast. The land was close on either beam. The small wooden
houses were catching the golden light of a spring sun; the green of
the fields was intense; the forests were flung over the lower slopes
like black shawls; the rocky foreshore was splashed by our widening
wake. Few people were there to watch us pass. Overhead, the sky
was bright and clear and friendly in its emptiness.

About two hours after leaving Harstad we went to action stations
and the *Southampton* swung eastward. Battle flags flew from the
yard-arms. Destroyers swept along close inshore, for the water was
deep right up to the barely visible line where the mountains met
their clear reflections. Close to my gun, I lolled on the rail and felt
very unwarlike. We were on a cruise. I could almost fool myself
into thinking that I had a cream-walled stateroom below and that at
any minute a steward would come up and bring my whisky and soda.
The slopes were very beautiful. There was a soft echoing silence
over the water which lay out of reach of the powerful hum of our
engines. And then I saw the long twin barrels of P.2 mounting
angled up against the sky . . .

We came up to the vicinity of Narvik at half-speed. A signal lamp
flashed from the shore, but it was all very still and deserted. Away
on our port side a rusted merchantman was leaning against the rocks,
her hull like a strip of autumnal leaves, her masts broken and
stunted. One of the destroyers went over to investigate the hulk.
Meanwhile, we had found our first target. It was another wreck, the
funnel and upperworks and bow of a sunken freighter. It looked
harmless enough, and we might well have swept past it without
another thought had not some death and glory German snipers,
hidden in the twisted steel, opened fire on us with rifles and light
machine-guns. The bullets spat against our sides and went sighing
over across the water. In answer, our oerlikons jerked out rapid
fire with their peculiar rhythmic thumping. But we had no time to
waste there, and one of the 6-inch turrets moved slowly in its arc.
The guns swung up and down like waving arms, steadied and
followed the director. We on the deck pressed cotton-wool into

our ears and waited. The German snipers must have been paralysed by the black mouths of those great guns staring them in the face at point-blank range. The sniping became erratic and ceased. There was a brief silence, and then the fire and smoke belched from the three 6-inch. The wreck was wreathed with white spray; it shuddered and slumped deeper into the water. The funnel had been blown to pieces. The bridgework collapsed as if made of cardboard. And then silence engulfed us once more. We heard the far-away rumble of a great echo, minutes later, growing more and more distant as it moved, like a brooding wind, deeper and deeper into the shadowed valleys.

We glided into a prearranged position at about ten minutes to zero hour. Not far to our west a destroyer lay motionless on the calm surface. We were broadside on to the land, and I had a clear view of the panorama. The British hill was slightly to my right, sloping gradually to a bumpy skyline. Around its base there came a white dusty road which led up to the German defensive positions in the town itself. To the left of the town the land climbed steeply to a vast heap of crags and peaks, but in the foreground there was a small flat piece of land, dotted with trees, a clear space of some ten or fifteen acres surrounding a wooden farmhouse. We were little more than one thousand yards from the closest shore, but there was no sign of life, no movement in the town or on the slopes. No doubt thousands of pairs of eyes watched us arrive, and for some we were like a prophecy of death; for others, a welcome right arm, a tonic. At any rate, our presence there intimated that battle was about to commence. The baton was raised.

It was up to the army to make the first move. We on watch beside our gun knew very little of what went on, but we did know that we would be useless until the enemy machine-gunners disclosed their positions. We knew also that some of our signallers were going ashore to act as links between the army command and our gunnery officer. Semaphore was to be used. Apart from climbing up and over the mountains, the Germans had an escape route through the railway tunnel which led to the valleys in the east. A Norwegian force was supposed to be waiting at the outer end of the tunnel, but this seemed uncertain.

In a soft grey light we watched the passing of zero hour and saw the first of the British troops appear on the side of their slope. Almost at once German tracers sailed with incredible slowness over the shadows of the town. Blue and red tracer formed a kind of moving rainbow above the wooden buildings. A tank appeared from the hills to the west, rumbled up to the corner and stopped. After a few minutes it fired towards the town and then moved forward a few yards.

From the stalls we could see the Germans running from cover to cover, taking up their defensive positions. We could see the British troops advancing down the hill, having considerable difficulty with the German cross-fire. Ten minutes later the naval bombardment started. Our 6-inch guns opened up and the destroyer to starboard began desultory fire. Even then we seemed remote from the battle. We could see the shells flying off through the air and the sound of their explosion against the mountain face was like a great thunder blast which rolled and burst from valley to valley far beyond. The tank was moving up the road in fits and starts.

At first it seemed as if our gunnery control officers were selecting their targets visually. A German platoon raced for a small wooden building near some trees. Seconds later a 6-inch shell burst a few yards to the right of the building. A German sniper was sending tracer streaming from one of the taller rooftops in the town. Our guns dropped three shells on top of him. A fire flickered. Smoke clouds rolled up into the windless air. The destroyer spouted smoke from her forward turrets. Our soldiers were still pinned to the scrub on the western slopes.

Policy changed after the first hour. We shelled the railway tunnel and then sent salvos crashing straight into the mountain above the enemy position. Tons of rock rumbled downwards and clouds of thick yellow smoke covered the lower air. The German fire slackened and the tank was at the town's outskirts. The smoke was thick and black overhead and the flames were licking up like the tentacles of a giant squid.

Our role as spectators changed abruptly when the first enemy aircraft swooped low and dropped a stick of bombs across the calm waters. We had no time to look shorewards. We ran and loaded and fired and felt the ship turn and swing and shudder. Sometimes on my way from the hoist to the guns, I saw the black water spouting great walls of seething white. A destroyer would seem hidden, sunk, and then she would appear, still firing upwards with venom. We heard the sudden whistling of the bombs and crouched, waiting, and then the explosions came and the ship was shaken and drenched, but unharmed. It was a hectic day, but we heard that Narvik was in our hands and everything seemed worth while. Limp and exhausted, we sat on the deck and were thankful to see the last of that place as the ship turned and swung for the open sea and the smoke cloud grew faint above the mountain peaks.

It turned out that the capture of the port made little difference to the general trend of the campaign. We returned to Harstad and a few days later were preparing the complete evacuation. France was in danger. The focus had shifted. For the last melancholy hours we spent the time driving lorries into the fjord and scuttling ships and removing breeches from the long-barrelled 3-inch army guns. When all was clear we slipped out of that deep water for the last time. I think we were the last ship to steam from the Vest-fjord. On the way home we were bombed continuously and one of the escorting destroyers came in to Scapa Flow with her quarter deck under water. No one was sorry to see the last of the eastern side of the North Sea.

*   *   *

In those tense summer months when France collapsed and Dunkirk was on everyone's lips, the *Southampton* was at short notice for sea; she was keyed up for anything that came her way and often slipped through Hoxa boom to investigate or escort or rescue. There was the night when we raced out into a dense fog to intercept some enemy minesweepers which had been reported heading for Iceland. Visibility was down to two hundred yards and we saw nothing of the ship ahead but the white flicker of the water around the fog buoy she towed astern. We had not gone far when there was a turn to port, a wide turn which brought us up to the northward course. As we swung I saw the slim shape of a destroyer to starboard, a shape which sheered away and vanished into the murk. But the second cruiser in the line, the *Glasgow*, went head-on into the destroyer *Imogen* and sank her in a matter of minutes. It was one of those misfortunes of war, something which radar and R/T could have prevented had they been in use.

There was the time when, together with the cruiser *Coventry*, we steamed out towards Stavanger to try and find the submarine *Shark* which was in difficulties. We did not find her, but the enemy found us and we fired our 4.7's until the shadows of night rolled up and the guns were so worn that the shells seemed to sail out of the barrels in mad somersaults. In September, when the air battles were being fought out over London and the invasion was imminent, we went down to Sheerness and patrolled the eastern approaches to the Straits of Dover by night. By day we lay at anchor and I have vivid memories of black formations of German bombers, swooping down the river on their way home, just above our masts, and the short-range weapons spitting thousands of bullets into the dark fuselages. There was the German fighter which had engine trouble overhead and glided down above the merchant ships. Every vessel there let fly with 4-inch, 3-inch, oerlikon and machine-guns. Even rifles were fired. The fighter's engine recovered when the plane was about one hundred feet from the water and the machine shot headlong into one of the petrol tanks on the foreshore.

At the end of September, when things were quiet, we went back to Scapa Flow and lay for the short cool autumn days between the purple heather and the slate-grey of the sea. At the end of the month I left the ship and travelled down to Brighton to take a course for a commission as a sub-lieutenant in the Volunteer Reserve.

*   *   *

One evening in February 1941, Sub-lieutenant B. and I reached Southampton by train. In our new uniforms, however narrow and wavy the gold braid, we felt like characters from a comic opera. We felt self-conscious, but no one looked at us. Either we appeared normal, or the citizens of Southampton were accustomed to comic-opera dress in their midst. Anyway, the effect was the same.

After passing our exams and having a short leave, we had reported for duty, equipped and ready for anything. Most of us had been asked to state some sort of preference with regard to our future appointment. One had asked for destroyers and had been sent to a Fleet Air Arm base. One had asked for an M.L. and had been sent to a battleship. I had kept my mouth shut and had been sent to a mystery vessel called the *White Bear*. I met B. on the station. It appeared that he had been appointed to the *White Bear* also.

The naval offices were closed by the time we reached Southampton, and so, keeping a careful log of our expenses, we checked in at a gaudy hotel and had an excellent dinner. We felt fine. We felt finer still when a chance remark brought the information that the *White Bear* was a small motor yacht of about ten tons and that she had been run up and down the Solent on various duties until striking a submerged wreck. She had just come out of dock and was sitting down by the repair yards awaiting a coat of paint. B. and I were thrilled. We could see at once that such a vessel would not need two officers, and that we could work a highly satisfactory routine of week on, week off. This would bring us twenty-six and a half weeks' leave a year. B. was engaged, and demanded thirty weeks' leave in which to press home his private affairs. I granted him this, and we drew out our plan on the tablecloth.

As sub-lieutenants we felt rich, our pay being three pounds a week. Our mess bills would probably come to three or four pounds a month and our wine bills about two pounds a month. That would leave us six pounds a month to play with. We sucked the ends of our pencils and began to see the disadvantages about a large amount of leave, disadvantages about being officers at all. But the life ahead seemed full of promise and we went up to bed with a laugh in our hearts.

Next morning an extremely angry duty officer at the naval base stared icily at our smug faces and told us that by some misfortune there were two *White Bears* in the Navy. He was fed up redirecting mail, telegrams, stores and men. Our ship, he informed us, was on the Clyde. Would we mind very much getting to hell out of his office and catching the first train north. Oh. And would we tell our future commanding officer that one or other of the *White Bears* would have to resign. The joke was wearing a bit thin. We said we would and departed.

The *White Bear* in which B. and I were to serve for nearly a year was a converted steam yacht, one of the largest of her kind in the world. She had at one time been the property of the Commodore of the New York yacht squadron and had been sold to the British Government for five shillings at the beginning of the war when United States citizens were not allowed to make gifts of war material. At the time of the sale she had been beautifully fitted out, but several months on the mud had done her no good and she had been stripped of all valuables by light-fingered officials who were furnishing their houses. However, there was no lack of comfort aboard. I shared the green cabin with B., and we felt rather like film actresses as we stared round the finely panelled cabin with its mirrors and laid-on water and wide bunks. Above the cabin flat there was a large saloon with square ports looking out on three sides. Abaft this was the royal suite, now the captain's quarters. Armament consisted of one very old 4-inch forward and a 25-pounder aft, a few depth charges, some Lewis guns and some rifles. We were not intended for offensive work, our job being to escort allied submarines from port to port and from port to sea, taking care that they were not sunk by any bomb-happy aircraft of Coastal Command. We were based in Holy Loch, across the water from the smoke of the Gourock chimneys.

I had mistakenly imagined that once one became an officer one would become responsible for some part of a ship or unit. But B. and I were treated like absolute illiterates; we found that in spite of all our training and courses and exams, we had to start at the bottom again. We had learned to be able seamen; we had learned to be cadets. Now we had to learn to be officers. I found myself assisting the 1st lieutenant in keeping the upper deck spick and span, a pale shadow, a kind of mute bos'n, completely ignored by the senior ratings whose routine was so efficient that any change in it meant that they had to think and was therefore fought with a kind of passive-resistance campaign. At sea I kept watch with a lieutenant R.N.R. whose opinion of the Volunteer Reserve was acid. He considered it an insult to his years at sea that he should be under the 1st lieutenant who was one of the "Wavy Navy." In many ways the *White Bear* probably had more personal problems than any other ship and the fact that we remained happy was due to our awareness of the facts.

The commanding officer was a regular; he had retired many years before, but had returned at the outbreak of war and had been chosen for this particular job because of his knowledge of submarines. The 1st lieutenant, B., and myself were R.N.V.R. The navigator and gunnery officers were R.N.R. The engineers were all drawn from the Merchant Navy. There were five of them, and owing to the drab state of the engines, they spent most of their time in overalls, working like blacks. There were no engine-room artificers to do the job, and it was the officers who had to crawl around with spanners and screwdrivers. This led to a spot of friction in the wardroom since the engineers drifted up from time to time, covered in grease from head to toe. The 1st lieutenant objected to this, and, rightly or wrongly, stuck to his guns. This battle came to the surface whenever we were bored. Luckily they worked us pretty hard and we were never long at anchor.

The spring and summer of 1941 brought many happy days. I came to know the waters, inlets, islands and headlands of the west coast, from Cape Wrath to Cape Cornwall. It was a fine summer, and we idled our way between heather and rock and field, steaming through the tide rips in the sounds of Mull and Islay and the Pentland Firth.

My first solo watch by day started as we were entering the Pentland Firth. It was a crisp warm morning with a calm sea and the mountains to the south pale behind a summer haze. The Orkneys were low and dark above the sparkle of the water. I leaned over the front of the bridge and watched the men working on the foredeck. Daylight gave me a feeling of confidence. The sound of the engines murmured and a slight steam leak in the copper pipe to the whistle made a faint shrill hiss that was so constant that after a while I ceased to hear it. But it remained a background of sound, and added to the atmosphere of peace. By day, it was possible to take a look at the chart without being blinded, and this made me more confident. The tides would find it difficult to take me unawares. By day, one could see any other ships that might become involved in our movements. By day, time had some meaning; it was on my side.

Half-way through my four hours' watch, I had to make my first important decision. Two destroyers appeared to port, both moving slowly to cross our bow, both engaged in gunnery exercises. Right ahead was the small vessel which was towing a target. We on the bridge could see the yellow-grey smoke blowing from the warships' guns and the white pyramidal splashes where the shells were falling. It was obvious that if we went on our indifferent way we would pass right between the guns and their target. I had two alternatives. Either we could go to port, and pass close to the destroyers, or we could go to starboard and risk being hit by a long-hop. I decided to go south to starboard, for there was more open water there, and in any case it would be a move away from Scapa Flow from which might emerge bigger and better trouble.

I think that there was one moment during the war when every conscript or volunteer felt at last that he had ceased to be a burden to the professionals. In the Navy there was often an overpowering desire to be trusted, to be allowed to do something useful. The officers and men of a ship are so much of a team that individual effort is sometimes unwanted. It can be destructive. Thus, a newly commissioned officer suffers pains of disenchantment when he discovers that his thin gold stripe does not mean that he has a free hand. However far he rises there is always a senior eye fixed upon him with benevolent watchfulness. The most one can achieve is to feel that the eye sometimes closes and that there is a mutual trust.

It may seem ridiculous to assert that an alteration of course to avoid two destroyers was either difficult or decisive, but when I gave the short order "Starboard fifteen" I felt just as pleased as might some newly appointed admiral when he first orders the Home Fleet to proceed to sea. How long ago it was when I had first been trusted to steer a four-masted barque in a rising wind, or furl a royal by myself, or fix a ship's position on the chart by simple cross-bearings. How distant seemed the trials and examinations and tests, the slow struggle for maturity, the hours in classrooms at Brighton while the war went on above, the days in Newhaven harbour when we learned to handle a ship by driving an old tug up and down the water, banging into everything in the way, bouncing crazily from one danger to another. We had more than ourselves to contend with at Newhaven because, as we discovered later, the tug's crew had sometimes been slow to obey our panicky order "Full astern," with the result that we had gone full-tilt into the wooden wharf and the tug had been docked and the crew had been given a little extra leave. But that was all past. The two-thousand-ton *White Bear* was swinging across the tide. In one short instant all the dry days of instructions were crystallised into action. The sun beat down and life was suddenly very pleasant indeed.

Life in port was gay; life at sea became interesting. Towards the end of the summer B. and I were given our watchkeeping certificates, pronounced able to keep a watch on surface vessels. This meant that we would probably be sent to something slightly more offensive. It meant that I was in a position to start training for submarines, that I would have to start all over again, ignorant, at the bottom of a new ladder. It meant also that I would see, through binoculars and periscope, the coasts of Spain and France, Corsica, Italy, Greece, Turkey and Syria. I would move to India and Ceylon, to Burma and Sumatra, to the waters around Australia,

Bali, Siam and the Philippines. It meant the enjoyment of great endeavour and great comradeship, the slow understanding of the subtle mixture of flippancy and keenness which forms the naval attitude.

There were throughout the war a variety of personal ambitions which were inseparable from the general idea of conquering an enemy. There was promotion. There was a remote chance of command. One might, if lucky, be handed one of the routine number of medals sent to the flotilla. Yet for the reservists the end was bound to come, and such dreams were of greater importance to the regulars, to those whose whole lives depended so much on where they stood at the war's end.

Looking back now, I see the war as a combination of college ball game and endurance test. I remember the lean boats of the submarine flotilla almost as I do the lean bodies of a cross-country running team at school. I can at times relive those moments when the boat glided into a sun-drenched harbour and the three-week patrol had ended, the sweat and weariness and fear and anger had ended. In its place, we found friends; we heard the cheer which greeted our return; we glanced at the sailing boats. We relaxed as only those who have been strained for weeks can relax. That was our war. We knew the blasting heat of Beirut and the drive up to the cool white mists of the Syrian mountains; we knew the width of the Indian Ocean and the sun sheen on the glassy swell; we knew the kick of a bottle of Cyprian brandy warmed in tropical sands and the long days of abstinence when our eyes probed the enemy shoreline.

It was a life of contrasts, and within a short space of time we experienced the emotions of a lifetime. Bodies and minds were tuned to the swift pace, to the effort of remaining normal through such variety of event. For me there was always the fight against the sea. There was the old horizontal navigation and later the vertical brand. There were storms and fogs and all the normal dangers of the oceans. A sailor is rarely killed by the enemy alone, but dies through a combination of enemy action and sea action. One aids the other.

Fear is a half emotion; it is born through an anticipation of the unknown, but evaporates when a man is face to face with something he can see. On the few occasions when I felt that there was no chance of surviving I felt no fear, only a great fierce anger. I remembered unfinished conversations, friends I wished to see again, ambitions not realised, a life horribly incomplete. Within the quick passing of such moments I cast aside all those false values which had until then bound me in their coils. It was as if my eyes could see out beyond the steel shell of the submarine, out through the hot water of the eastern seas, out to the shadowed surface of the spinning world. I gained no new virtues, learned no truths. It was a purely negative achievement. But I determined that if I was to survive I would start my life anew, retaining only those values and ideas which seemed constant to all ages, vital to all men.

When peace came I was without illusion. Demobilisation was like a release of gravitation, and I was dropped out into that blackness of space within which I sought my own star and my own free orbit.

CHAPTER NINE

BOATYARD

THE spring of 1946. Once again the water laps beyond thin planking and a tide flows. Once again I sleep in a narrow bunk and there are footsteps above, footsteps on a boat's deck. But there the resemblance to the past ends, for my post-war home is resting on the mud at low water and the sea is some miles down the river's course. She is called *Freak*, this aged houseboat, and in many ways the name is suitable. But the scene is dominated by boats; there are hundreds of them, and the *Freak* is not conspicuous in any way.

The dawn smell is one of damp earth, weed and, faintly, sawdust, fuel oil and fresh paint. The dawn light is pallid over a steel sheet of moving water, trees black and massed. The clouds are full of movement. The early mist creeps along the surface of the water, clinging, white, like rolling smoke. A mast protrudes here, a dinghy floats in disembodied solitude. A stick glides past, and a thinness in the drifting mist reveals a gold glitter of still water, a soft reflection of the rising sun.

I see all this through a circular port. The tide is out; the mud shines and the grasses are tall and still. There is a throbbing silence, sound stifled by the mist. Greyness; the shadows of trees and tall masts; the acrid smell of dead waters; a growing heat; the splash of hidden oars; a shrill distant siren; the deep rumble of traffic crossing a bridge upstream; a gathering jumble of sounds; the awakening of the riverside; the new day.

My cabin is very small, just a built-in bunk, a small table, and enough room to turn around between one bulkhead and the other. This is not an exotic houseboat, not full of cocktail cabinets and pianos. It is owned by Bill, who is a mechanic in the boatyard which sprawls along the right bank just upstream. Bill has been in the boatyard since he was a boy. Now, with his wife and child, he lives aboard the well-moored boat, walking to work along duckboards or rowing up in the tiny pram dinghy. He has put many hours of work into his home since he retrieved it from the Navy. The saloon is spick and span. The water tank is down aft, but a second tank sits on the top of the galley and the tap is gravity fed. Lights are Calor gas. The upper deck is fenced in, and here the young son has a giant play-pen. A plank leads ashore to a path that winds through the grasses and then climbs steeply to the tarmac road. The village is not far up the road, an old village, built on the site where the wooden ships of Nelson's fleet were hammered into shape. The river has narrowed; the water has receded. The old stone church once stood by the edge of the tide and the dark branches of the graveyard yew trees leaned out over the shallows, but the church is now distant; it can only just be seen from the low green waterside.

To Bill the morning on the river is just another day, very like many others that have gone before. He knows every reed, every stone. He reads a story in the mud-bound, bare-ribbed hulks that angle skywards from the rippling brown of the moving water. He looks out and sees a white spectre in the mist, a slim shape with the tide running in a black line from the stern. To me that is just a sloop-rigged five-ton yacht, a nameless plaything. To Bill it is much more. He knows the details of the engine, the reversible marine diesel; he knows the way the rudder is fitted and the intricacies of the steering gear; he knows the way the yacht's ribs are covered with planking; he knows that sometime, somewhere, a yard put iron fastenings in the planking and sees the tell-tale rivulets of rust on the white flank; he can appreciate the lines at a single glance, and is glad he won't have to go out in her with a choppy sea and a head wind and a flowing tide. He wipes his lean shaven jaw, and keeps a few secrets to himself. Perhaps he knows how much the owner has been charged for the boat's refit, and how much was the actual cost. Perhaps he knows that the engine is bound to fail if given a stiff test, and that the owner cannot afford a new one. . . .

It is six o'clock. The mist is lifting. The sheds of the yard are visible, and beyond, the new stone bridge is a shadow between unseen banks. Buses and lorries cross the bridge. We hear them, their gear-changing and their whining; they are the reason for the ceaseless alteration in the indistinct shape of the bridge. A sudden ray of sunlight strikes the water close at hand, and the surface is like thin milk, creased by frail strings of weed and grass pulled out from the bank. A launch passes in midstream. It is heard, a low hum. I strain my eyes to see it, but there is nothing, nothing but the crisp waves of the wake that come out towards me and flutter on the edge of the mud.

I am a newcomer to the yard, one of three in my age group who have decided to learn the business of building and repairing small boats, and later designing them. In many ways, we are all too old to start, but start we must. We could almost be the fathers of the apprentices; we could be the sons of the skilled workers, the trade unionists who fix us with a grim eye. We are not quite certain what we are or where we stand. For lack of a better name, I have called myself a painter. For my labours I receive three pounds a week. The day begins at seven o'clock sharp.

Bill and I meet out in the crisp air, a spring air, but one that still holds a touch of winter, for the mist shrouds us with a cool damp-ness, and it is only the knowledge of the height of the sun that makes us feel the warmth. Our footsteps sound on the deck. Our sand-wiches are in our pockets. As we go down the gangway and across the duckboards, the sweetness of the mud and the young grass and the rotting wood of the hulks is in our nostrils.

It is only a two-minute walk to the yard, two minutes up the edge of the river. As we approach we see the dim shapes of the yachts, barges and landing craft, all bows up on the soft mud, masts thin and frail, ropes like spiders' webs, shining in the golden light. The sun is trying to come through, it sheds a mellow glow down to the white of the river and the grass glows like a stream of emeralds.

Near the office Bill leaves me and goes off to his own work. The office . . . it is a ramshackle houseboat, paint that was once white peeling off in long blisters. I know what goes on inside. It is the goal of all those who have bought cheap yachts and hope to have them made seaworthy, the goal and the death-cell. Hope is often lost in that office, for prices of material and labour, excepting myself, are high. A mere sniff at a boat will cost ten pounds. We can see them come out, faces low, brows creased; they are ex-Army and ex-Air Force officers, a smattering of ex-Navy, but surprisingly few. They idle by the edge of the mud and ponder. Sometimes they go back to the office and the boat is taken in hand. More often their craft swing at buoys in the tide, a perch for the gulls, desolate ruins which were once pictured in a glory of paint, beneath the gilded Mediterranean sky. All this we can watch.

The office itself is a long wide room, papers lying all over the place, nuts and bolts covering the floor, blocks and rope and wires heaped in all corners. It is like a junk shop, a ship chandler's back room. There is a desk and even a telephone, but the business is run by word and deed. Paper and pen are used as little as possible. The yard, now running for several hundred yards along the bank, is the outcome of a gratuity of the First World War, immense hard work and a good deal of hard bargaining.

On this morning I await orders, not sorry to be kept hanging around under the young sun, for the mist has risen clear of the water and I can stand and look out across to the opposite bank. I can see the grey shapes of the old M.L.s on which lives a floating population. I can see the silver of the river as it winds upstream, up to the beech trees and oaks and maples, to the wooded banks which are undisturbed except by birds and rabbits and water rats. The light is now peeping through the sheds which are open to the river. The dusty forms of the yachts, mostly sheathed in tarpaulin, are half-seen. They are chrysalises, awaiting our helping hands, awaiting the casting off of the sheath, the licking down, the loosing and spreading of wings. . . .

Old Harry comes up behind me; he is one of the oldest men in the yard, but his eyes twinkle. He wears an old beret over his grizzled hair. His lips curve into the wrinkles of his flat cheeks. "Come on," he says. "You and I work on *Diana* to-day. *Diana*'s bottom." He chuckles and hands me a scraper. "Do you know how to use that?"

"It looks," I say, "as if there is only one main way to use it. Up and down. Back and forth." I move the scraper as if taking a layer off the belly of the white clouds.

Harry grimaces and leads me to where *Diana* sits on the wooden slip, sheltered from sun and wind by the largest of the sheds. The boat looks in a bad way; she is a forty-five foot motor yacht, white hulled, teak railed, with a cabin up forward. Her stern is partially dismantled so that the engineers can get to the rudder controls. But that is not our part of *Diana*'s beautifying. We, Harry and I, are only concerned with the hull. It certainly needs paint, and it will need a scrape first. But on this first morning I doubt very much whether the boat will shine very brightly again. I remark on this to Harry who puts his head on one side and observes me in penetrating silence. At ten minutes past seven we started work.

At once I see that my scraper is not quite so useful as Harry's. It does not move so smoothly or so evenly. It takes away chunks of paint and leaves as many chunks. My arm grows tired. Harry pulls his blade along the hull with a minimum of effort and a maximum of achievement. We move away from one another, for I have taken the starboard side while he works on the port. All the time while I sweat and struggle I can hear the soft rhythm of his strokes. At length, pretending to look for a rag, I move across the bow until I can study Harry's technique. A straight pull, pressure applied with the left hand, a stroke with the grain, a use of the scraper edge here and there, a use of body weight instead of arm muscle. I return to my side and progress to my satisfaction. One hour passes. Two hours. At nine o'clock I move off to have a cup of coffee in the shipwrights' ship. This is perfectly legal, but Harry scoffs and makes some rude remarks about ex-servicemen. I feel his eyes on me as I walk down the duckboards and my tail is between my legs.

To my relief I find Bill having coffee. He and six other men sit on the benches and chat. My conscience is clear, but I have a feeling of urgency, for Harry will have finished the port side soon and I want my side all to myself. I hurry back to *Diana*, my lips burned with boiling coffee. I feel immensely happy when I find the scraper beginning to become a useful weapon against the layers of thick paint.

And so it goes on. Bill and I walk back to the *Freak* for lunch, returning to our work an hour later. The sun is high; the mist is a white screen of clouds; the tide floods up between the boats, covers the mud and laps at the lower part of the office. Rowing-boats pass to and from the shore as some of the women from the houseboats come to land with their shopping-baskets. A man in a khaki shirt sits on the deck of his converted barge and eats an apple, his eyes fixed appreciatively on a freshly varnished skylight. A grey-haired man walks up and down the deck of a large landing craft, muttering to himself, occasionally glancing at a piece of paper. He is working out the best way to turn this instrument of war into a home. The lorries roar over the bridge. Over the hills there sounds a deep full-throated boom. We all stop to listen. Yes. There it is again, the *basso profondo* of the *Queen Mary*.

Harry and I scrape away until half-past three when we down tools for a cigarette and a cup of tea. By now the *Diana* looks perfectly hideous, her sides are pock-marked and rough. Bare planking is dark. An undercoat shows pale yellow. Last year's enamel is grey and dusty. Harry, who sees progress, cocks his head on one side and grunts. "Mm. Coming on. Coming on." We lower our heads over the teacups but regard *Diana* from under our eyebrows. Almost before we are aware that noon has passed, the shadows of evening are closing in and the river is like a strip of gunmetal. The anchored yachts swing to the tide's change; they seem to pivot around the rigid reflections of masts. A coolness flows from the water; the reeds are like strips of frozen metal; later a light suddenly flicks on in one of the houseboats and its reflection stabs· at us like a blade of bronze. Our scrapers defy the shadows; they work away in a misty half-darkness. Sounds come clearly as sight fades. A car rumbles up the hill beyond the village. A train rattles; an engine whistles; someone is hammering in the next shed; a figure passes along the duckboards, humming, regular footfalls; a duck calls; dogs bark suddenly, several of them together; the houseboat wireless sends out strains of jazz; Harry spits briskly . . .

It is seven o'clock when the work ends, for we do an extra hour on overtime. My arm aches infernally. I take the scrapers back to the store and make for home. At the edge of the river it is grey and sombre and quiet. The water is receding from the mud. The tops of the trees seem to brush the moving clouds. The deserted boats are forlorn and cheerless now that the sun has departed. There will be no stars to-night. On either side of the boards across which I walk back to the *Freak* the marsh is black and even and flat. The last ice-blue light of day filters down through the dark sky and tinges the river's edge, a near white reflection beyond the skeleton hulks, beyond the thin grasses. Night comes in from the east, bringing a soft cold wind that flutters the water around *Freak*'s lower hull and makes the tree branches swing. The night mist is almost like a rain in my face. It is good to climb the narrow sloping gangway and reach out for the door handle. It is good to walk into the warm light saloon and leave the river to the mist and wind and swift cloud shadows.

*   *   *

During those days, when the mists of winter were growing thinner and the trees along the riverside were tinged with their first green, Harry and I concentrated on *Diana's* hull. This was not, on first sight, a highly skilled job, but I discovered that there was a great deal more in it than just scraping off paint and brushing it on again. Success was not seen in terms of increased wages, but it showed in an owner's eye.

Harry was one of the old school; he worked long and hard, driven on by a real pride in his accomplishments. Nothing was too much trouble for him and only perfection made him pleased. As the days passed, I began to see that his methods achieved results. We scraped and sandpapered that hull until it was as smooth as a table top. We went over the whole thing with detailed thorough-ness, filling any minute holes or cracks with putty and then smoothing once again. We sandpapered before applying the first coat of underpaint and then sandpapered again. Once an even surface was there we put on three coats of thin white paint and stood back to see how she shaped. Harry nodded and decided that we could start with the enamel the next morning.

For the last stage we needed sunlight, for the enamel goes on easily if the planks have a little warmth in them. On a cold day the brush is like an iron weight and it takes the strength of a right arm to keep the surface smooth. Luckily a clear sky showed at sunrise and the morning was bathed in a soft heat, the heat of late May. By the following afternoon our job on *Diana* was finished, and we could relax outside the shed between the washing tide and the slip, noticing how the hull shone as if wet, how it was like glass in its evenness and how the light, reflected from the water, danced up and down the curve of the planking. "All right," Harry said. "That's enough for to-day. To-morrow's Sunday, you know."

Sunday. It was one of those days when the air is keen and cool before sunrise and the day's heat is in the rays of the sun. At breakfast time the river was like a white road and the rowing-boats moved slowly upstream, leaving a thin black line astern. It was going to be hot.

At ten o'clock I went down to the *Freak*'s blunt stern and stepped aboard the brown-painted dinghy. My lunch was in my pocket. Pushing off, I rowed slowly up past the deserted yard, up under the bridge and into the quiet reach of the river where the trees came down to the grass banks. From inland came the soft clamour of church bells. My oars moved in a small arc; the bow plunged into the calm, almost virginal surface; the small brittle sounds of the village, a shout, a laugh, a dog's bark, were left astern and there was nothing to hear but the washing of the water and the rhythmic thud of the oars in the stirrup. The land glowed green, the tops of the woods running up slopes on either side with the flat wide stretch of foreshore cut by shining creeks and black inlets between the tall grass.

I looked over the side and let the boat drift. Somewhere beneath

me lay the wreck of the *Grace de Dieu*, the ship w
had had built in 1418 and which had been burned in
at low water, her oak planks were still lying in the mu
I did not find her that day and rowed on around a bend
curve of the main stream swept close up to the trunl
and the water poured over the gravel bed. Here in the soft green
light of the leaf shade I moored to an overhanging root and climbed
ashore. Lying on my back, eyes shut, I listened to the music of the
river and the sudden jarring call of a jay and the splash as a water rat
dived in from the grass verge. It was for me a timeless moment, a
moment when life seemed halted and the past and future were
drawn together into a complete picture. What had gone before,
days at sea, school, peace, war and return, were one with my hopes
and dreams. I realised then that routine and a swift flow of life tend
to lead to blindness, causing a man to believe that what is past is
past and can have no bearing on the future. But even the stabs of
fate which bring sudden success or black failure have some seed in
the past. Realisation of this comes at the times when the present
ceases to move and achieves a timelessness which must be divorced
from all things physical.

After that Sunday I began to enjoy the work at the yard, because I
understood how past experiences could be made to help in many
ways. Whether it was rowing, mooring a boat, painting the inside
of a landing craft, rigging a yacht, or even just standing and watching
the river scene, I was able to draw on a supply of knowledge which
had been almost instinctive and which had slipped to the back of my
mind. I was able too to see a little more in the future than just the
definite fact of next payday, or perhaps the fear of no payday. The
future became solid, because I saw that it was already a part of me.
In war one had learned not to think far ahead. Peace had brought a
good deal of political fervour which at first had seemed a good thing,
able to increase one's hopes, but this was not true. The inconstancy
of politics became plain from the actions of the politicians themselves, who hurried to complete various measures before elections,
and by people who lived in fear of the election and fought to make

much as they could while their particular party was in power. But I wanted to look further ahead than five years; I wanted to find something, some sheet-anchor which would hold through wars and political storms and personal crises. Harry, old and proud of his skill, had stability, and Bill, comparatively young but confident, had stability. I think that their secret lay in the fact that they had combined independence with unselfishness; they accepted the fact that no luck, no politics, no charity, would make a lasting difference to their lives. The foundation at least would have to come from their work. Once they had established their own personal independence they were willing to share responsibilities. Their work was their sheet-anchor, and they were only too pleased to let it serve others less fortunate.

I learned many things while at the yard. It was during those spring months that I began to consider my old ambition, to write books. After supper, alone in the warmth of the saloon, I used to sit down and scribble out chapters of a novel, page after page of words, sentences, grammar, syntax, punctuation, description, style, characterisation and design. I found at first that it was almost impossible to concentrate on one thing at a time. A theme was swallowed by the story or vice versa. A character was hopelessly inconstant. Descriptive passages refused to fit smoothly between pieces of dialogue. Hundreds of new problems arose as I pressed on. Undreamed-of difficulties became apparent.

As is so often the case, the decisive question, whether to write or design yachts, was answered for me. One morning two letters arrived. The first was from a publisher who considered that some notes I had written on my experiences in submarines would, if revised, make a book which they would consider accepting. The second letter was from a firm of boat builders for whom I had arranged to work. They were very sorry, they wrote, but various difficulties made it impossible for them to develop their business as had been planned, and therefore they would be unable to offer me a position. The various difficulties, I discovered later, were simple. The firm had gone bust.

The cross-roads at which I stood were right-angled. Ten years at sea could lead to some sort of work which would not be completely new. On the other hand, the war had shown that the average man can do any job, providing the opportunity arises or it is a matter of necessity. If I turned to writing, the sea experience would still be valuable. In any case . . . But it was no good prolonging the argument. A pint of beer at the Jolly Sailor clinched matters.

I arranged to go to Cornwall in the summer.

CHAPTER TEN

FALSE DAWN

VINE COTTAGE stood high on the eastern side of the village, only a rocky path between the front wall of the small garden and the cliff edge. From its windows I looked across the cove, the boats, the thatches and the rocks, to the distant headland from which the Lizard light shone after dark. My old love Caerleon lay a mile to the east.

There is a strange silent emptiness about living alone. No sound comes from those rooms which lie beyond the open door. No voice could intrude. However busy one may be, there are certain hours when everything seems pointless. I painted out the small kitchen a stark white, so that it looked large and cool; I wandered along the meandering path on the cliff; I cooked and ate my solitary meals; I wrote and listened to the radio, messed about in the garden, worked and slept. There were few idle moments, but the times when life seemed unbearably flat and dull were always there. They were like stretches of a straight road that runs between mud flats and barren skylines; they refused to be kept at bay by an awareness of their cause.

It was a hot calm summer. Sometimes I used to climb out into the green dawn and walk down to the beach, going off in a small grey crabber called *Ocean Pride* and returning in time for a late lunch. Out on the water, the day arrived over the eastern horizon and we could see it strike the land in a sudden patch of green and brown. The water, white and still in the early hours, was splashed with a faint blue. And then it deepened until it held the full tone of the cloudless sky.

In the heat of the afternoon I retreated indoors into the liquid cool of the shadows, within which it was possible to think and work and read until the evening off-shore breeze came down from the heath.

By then it was nearly time to have supper and start the two com-
paniable hours in the pub, when beer slipped down our parched
throats and there were games of darts and talk and laughter and
innumerable fishermen's tales. At ten when the bar emptied there
were gruff good-nights under the white stars, a pause to watch the
silver of the moon on the sea and to follow the lights of a liner
speeding homeward, and then I climbed up the steep path to
silence. The day's end would be warm and comfortable, a lamp
burning behind my shoulder, a pen in my hand and a book on my
knee, and the window wide open to the hushed summer night.

There are a great many facets to the Cornish scene. There are
grey-stone market towns, bright holiday resorts, villages full of
retired generals and dentists and solicitors with large villas and
modernised cottages and much respectability. There are villages
full of artists, with lofts and barns converted into studios and a great
deal of whitewash and clematis and thatch and forced temperament.
Our little village seemed unchanged; it had not been discovered;
it pivoted around the fishermen and anyone who thought they could
alter that were in for a rough time. Beyond the old nucleus of small
cottages there were a few more modern houses in which lived the
sons and daughters of the fishermen, men who worked on the roads,
farmed, worked in the town or on the new airfield, and the women
who "took in visitors" during the summer. There were a boat-
builder, a market gardener, a carpenter, an ex-naval electrician, a
taxi-driver and a postman. They were all a part of the community,
but it was the fishermen who were responsible for the village's
existence.

Once or twice during July the amateurs took out two of the
crabbers and went along to Kennack sands with an eighty-foot
ground net. The professionals watched us with a kind of amused
disinterest. This was week-end fishing, often by moonlight, but it
entailed plenty of preparation and hard work.

". . . To-night is the night. Half an hour after sunset it is decided
that we take the next tide and go to action stations at 1 a.m. The
owner of the net is in charge; he suggests that one crabber, towing

a small boat in which is the net, leaves the village at about one. He himself will drive the second party down to the beach. Moonrise is at oo o5. We will have plenty of light. We are all a little military in our planning, Johnny the builder, just back from the 8th Army, Arthur, carpenter, home from Berlin, and the others all recently demobilised from one service or other. We try to visualise all details and leave nothing to chance. The fish no doubt will spoil everything, but we can only do our best. The fish are the hostile forces.

"The volunteers gather on the stony beach at half-past midnight. The moon has risen, but it is still below the top of the cliff. Its light shines on the cottage walls behind us and the village has a Christmas-card look, a blue whitewash slapped over everything. A window reflects the moon which we cannot see, a square of cold gleam. The sea looks very flat and black and shining, like one of Hollywood's expensive glass dance floors. We gather around the boat, leaning on it for a minute or two while the petrol tank is filled and a few last adjustments made. And then the crabber slides down the timbers to the white glitter of the tide edge; it grates over the last strip of shingle, splashes quietly, and slides outward, buoyant, swinging slowly. The dinghy lies at anchor, the ground net heaped up like a load of coal. After a great deal of gruff cursing, advice, jokes and banter, we are all aboard, the dinghy astern, and the engine *phut-phut-phutting* away like a distant motor-bike. The village drops away surprisingly fast and abruptly we come out into the full moonlight and can see how swiftly we pass through the water and how wide and white is the wake. There is nothing more to do now for half an hour or so until we reach the shallow water off the beach. . . ."

A hundred yards out from the centre of Kennack sands we dropped anchor and looked around. The bay swept out on either side. Right ahead, the stretch of sands gleamed white and clean and the waves broke in a great even curve. Beyond, there was a dark valley with cornfields and woods and a shadowed emptiness. No house was in sight.

Our problem was simple. We had a wide stretch of shallow water ahead, almost free of rocks, running clear to the sands. The net was ten feet deep and eighty feet long. It was weighted at the bottom and had cork floats along the top. One end of it would be dropped towards the western end of the beach, one end to the east. From each end a rope would be led ashore and then the hauling would start, and the net would become a great crescent, the horns on the sand and the arc in the water. We would slowly haul it in, heaving and straining until the bag was reduced to a shallow space and the fish were visible as they turned their white under-bellies to the moon.

It was a simple enough plan, but as in war the staff were confused by simple snags. First there was some difficulty in finding the end of the net, which had been stowed in the boat by sunlight. And then when the eastern end was in the water a long pause showed that there was something wrong. A shout echoed out across the stillness of the bay. What was that? The net was too shallow or the water too deep. Very well. We would have to allow some of the fish to slip away over the top. It could not be helped. We could see the second team arriving on the sand, their shadows immensely long and thin, their cigarette ends glowing fitfully. Some of them began to throw stones at some hidden target. Men passing away idle minutes. . . .

"All is set at last. The ropes are ashore and we have all gathered on the beach and step softly over the dry sand. The crabber lies at anchor, a coal-black shape on the ice-white of the moonpath. The dinghy circles the outside of the net, the oars moving and glinting. There are seventeen of us, nine for one rope, eight for the other. We divide in silence and walk over to where the long snake of hemp lies across the sand like a black tidemark. On the misty horizon there are two yellow mast-lights as a ship slips down the last hour of the Channel. A bird calls shrilly, suddenly. Someone slams the car door. The waves come in like creases of ebonite and then break, first in the centre and then outward, glistening circles of phosphorescence.

"It is about two o'clock when we take up the damp rope and begin to haul. Anything may happen now. It is quite possible that the preliminary reconnaissance was not thorough and that there are in fact small sharp rocks out there on which the net will catch and break. The important thing is that both ropes come in evenly, and to ensure this the owner of the net stands in the middle and calculates and admonishes. He it is who keeps his eye on the top of the net, making sure that it is above water. If we haul the net into too much of a circle, the centre will sag. If we haul outward, the bottom may be clear of the sand. It is a question of fine adjustment.

"Fine adjustment, however, is almost impossible when seventeen men are hauling on heavy ropes and the tide is in the net and the weed makes the whole thing weigh heavily downwards. We pause, and see what is happening. The weed has taken charge and is gathering in the bight of the net, dragging the cork floats under the surface. The man in the boat slaps his oars at escaping fish; he shouts. Unless something is done quickly, we shall have an empty bag. We all seem to get the same idea at once, and rush into the shallows and plunge our hands and arms into the water, groping around, feeling a slim slippery shape, clutching and lifting and throwing back to the clear sand. Someone gathers up the fish and slings them into a heap. We are all soaked and sweating and half-angry as the fish go sliding over the top of the sagging net. The man in the boat is laughing aloud. A torch beam flicks on to the scene and the moonlight is suddenly thin and white and cold . . ."

That night we caught four bass, fifteen mackerel, five plaice, twelve ray, two wrasse, and some smaller fish which were left on the sand to await the fast-rising tide. It was not a great bag, but it was worth a night out of bed, and there was something quite perfect in the easy trip home with the dawn pale over the stern and the moon behind a screen of high cloud and the lighthouse flashing and the cove dark and peaceful and still with the white of the cottages standing out like square sails. We came in to the beach, wood on shingle. The winch rattled and the boat moved slowly up towards the road. I went up my path, up the steep slope above the tinted water to the gate into the garden, the door into the house, and the stairway that led upward to my waiting bed.

Before I slept I heard the fishermen go down in the dawn light and the boats moving off over the pallid green water. The flicker of the lighthouse on the ceiling grew fainter and fainter.

*   *   *

I rarely moved from the village during the summer months, and yet my mind was often far out over the horizon. I wondered what had happened to the Finns with whom I had sailed, and whether the blonde skipper of a Norwegian fishing boat was still guiding her craft up the dark angles of Vestfjord and why I had had no word from a friend who had gone out to China to help the Chinese customs fight pirates. My greatest approach to civilisation was up the path to the little shop and post-office. In other directions I could walk for miles along the cliff without meeting a soul, or take the dinghy out along the shore and drop a rock anchor while swimming, and climb up the cliffs to dive down again into the unrippled water.

My friends in the village were refreshingly devoid of any sort of snobbery, and their criticism of art and literature was revealing. Painters were always messing about in odd corners, men and women who arrived by car, bicycle or on foot, and set up their easels in the shade. The cove watched them from afar. "They can't paint," one of the old fishermen said. "We have had a few good ones down. But not many. There was one old man who used to sit in the corner of the pub and sketch us. He was good. Yes. Nothing to beat him."

"What was his name?" I asked.

"Why, I couldn't remember. Yes. Wait. It were John. Yes, I believe. Augustus John. Ever hear tell of him?"

"Yes," I said. "I have."

The village had a keen sense of judgment, particularly when it came to snap decisions on character. They cared nothing for money

155

or position or looks. Their first impressions went right down to bedrock and they looked into a man's eyes, at his hands and at his lips. Then came the judgment. They liked him or they didn't like him. There were no considerations. In the same way they considered that outsiders were bound to be slightly inferior. No visitor would know anything about the items that mattered, the local tides, weather, fishing prospects, beer prospects or the way to cut willows for the pots. The stark sincerity of the place made newcomers seem as artificial as plastic dolls.

In this atmosphere of pleasant reality I began to read seriously; the Bible, Walter Pater, Conrad, Dostoievsky, Proust, Ruskin, Dickens, Hardy, Melville, Pepys, Carlyle, Stevenson, and a great many others, ancient and modern, light and serious, fantastic and factual. To my surprise and relief I discovered that most of the writers who were now part of one's education had written for a living and had often been both poor and badly received in their day. This fact seemed to confound all those who pretended that authors should divorce commerciality from their art. When at first I had announced that I was going to write, come what may, all the old clichés were forthcoming. "You must have a private income." "You will never write anything good if you are happy." "You won't get anywhere unless you know at least three critics, old boy." "You simply can't write for a living. It just isn't done." "But you never went to a university." "But you were never a miner." "But . . . but . . . but . . ." And so it went on.

I used to wake when the sun was just sliding around the corner of the window. Mrs. B. next door would already be shaking a mop into the morning air, and there would be steps on the hard path, and noises from the beach. Looking out, I saw the bright colours of the wild flowers along the edge of the steep cliff, pink and yellow and white, loosestrife, mallow, cliff daisy, marigold and wild rose.

There was colour, and a feeling of spaciousness. If I drew back a few feet into the small room, the window frame held a picture of sky and sea, a quiet, blue emptiness. In the garden below the veronica was a mass of deep purple and the geraniums splashed scarlet and the rose over the door trailed against the cream walls.

The friendship of the Cornish is slow to mature. It does not leap up and engulf one, but keeps its distance. For a long time a new-comer is greeted politely and quickly and left to go on his way. No one interferes with him. No one expects great familiarity. And then one day there is a change in the air which is as subtle as a change of wind. The morning smile is broader and the idle talk becomes broken by moments of companionable silence. The politeness remains, but it is different; it is suddenly a help and not a hindrance. A single word indicates that a mutual trust has been established and that the last barrier is down. Once found, the Cornish friendship is as solid and lasting as a granite cliff.

When I sauntered down to the tap to fill my earthenware pitchers it always took half an hour, for the Cornish do not hurry over their "good mornings," believing that God made plenty of time for us all. If I went over to the shop for the morning paper, it took at least an hour. It was useless trying to hurry, and after a while I discovered that there was indeed plenty of time. Life was ruled by the wind and the tides. Even if one wanted the taxi to go to a train or run over to Falmouth, it was necessary to find out what the forecast was, for the driver went out in one of the crabbers, and if the tide was late he would not be free until well after noon. The local bus passed within half a mile of the village; it wandered around, back and forth, in and out, taking nearly an hour to do the eight miles into the market town that lay inland. The summer months held a pleasant atmosphere of the warm indolent south, of minutes leaning over the side of a boat and contemplating the floorboards in silence, of sitting on the rocks and observing the passing ships through half-closed eyes, of cows wandering on the dry grass and butterflies flickering against the yellow-green of the palm fronds, of the whitewashed walls cut by acute-angled shadows, and the strong invigorating smell of fish when the nets were trailing from boat to boat and from post to post, hanging to dry in the windless air.

In October we had our first gale. For six hours the glass had been dropping and the sky looked sullen and the sea grey. It was cold at night. The gulls were gathered on the cliff faces. The pine trees behind the cottage stood very still, but they whispered and sighed, and the smoke from the village chimneys circled and flew. The fishermen stood around in groups and looked towards the south-west.

The wind came at dusk; it was at first a gentle hum in the telephone wires, a quick sharp slapping of water on the shingle. By the time I switched out the last light and looked from my window towards the night, the water was fierce and white below the rocks and the thunder of the waves drowned the wind. On the beach, torches flashed and the winch rattled as the boats were pulled up towards the road, moved into a compact group well clear of the reaching sea. For a long time I lay in the darkness and listened to the rising strength of the black storm. The cottage seemed to tremble; the rain fluttered against the half-open window; the garden gate was banging back and forth. . . .

Dawn. The whole shape and size of the village seemed to have changed. Beyond the cottage roofs and the cliffs the sea was a tumult of grey and white, of waves that came in and burst over the cliffs, covering the black granite with a great whiteness and falling back in a hundred waterfalls. The shining blue backcloth I had always known had split and creased. Before, the village had seemed in the centre, a point where the road met the beach, where the boats and the cars connected. But now we were right on the edge, looking out at a liquid earthquake.

The wind made a difference to the village, for the fishermen might lose their pots and they were curt and tense. The doors were closed. The road up the steep hill was a mass of whirling dust. In the pub the silences were long between pessimistic cross-talk.

The subtle change in atmosphere made me realise how foreign that life was to me. It seemed, during those days, that all progress towards friendship had been halted, even put back. I was without knowledge of the language, of the customs, of the way of life. I lingered on the edge and tried in vain to see what passed behind the façade. My old friends there, men and women I had known since childhood, seemed preoccupied with the elements. My living did not depend on the wind, and therefore I did not matter.

Looking from my window, I saw the village as a clear-cut panorama of cliff and grass and beach and cottage. I wanted to make it serve as the background for a novel, but knew that the characters would have to be altered, for I knew too little about the fishermen's thoughts. Bit by bit, each day, I began to invent families to occupy the houses I could see. I imagined them moving about in wind and sun, drifting in and out of the late summer shadows. When I considered I knew their separate lives well enough, I began to sketch in a rough story, a thread on which to hang their actions. The days became solitary, but I never felt alone, for I had my friends with me, the friends who moved at my command and yet always seemed to surprise me in the end. I lived with them so much that I even found myself making references to them when talking to the fishermen, and had a sudden awareness of blank and puzzled stares.

It was a cold bleak autumn. Alone by the fireside I finished the book and flung it to one side to await brown paper, stamps, and the address of some publisher. Everything moved terribly slowly. The Virginia creeper over the porch began to turn red. The flowers withered and died in the cream-walled garden. The sea was restless. In a fit of black depression I re-read the book and discovered that I disliked it. Surely there should be some message in it, some comfort for anyone who might read it? What message? A victorious country was ruled by a victorious idealism. There was always a bitterness in such victories, and the old messages were now useless. Many people were writing about the horrors of war, but such things were lifted from behind a screen. Perhaps the greatest horror is the fact that the majority of people seemed to have enjoyed their war, found more in each other and themselves than they had expected. Reality is harsh, but, I thought, when a war is being fought it is fine and noble. When peace comes the writers dig down for all the latent horrors. When war approaches again, the horrors are forgotten and the old nobility is allowed to wax. It is a ridiculous cycle of ever-increasing ferocity.

My book went off without alteration, and reaching the end of my resources, I followed it by the next train. I left the village on a cold clear autumn day when the sea was like a white china floor and the ships seemed black and close and slow and the sound of the boats' engines came from behind the cliffs. I shut the cottage door behind me and walked up the hill to catch the bus. Everything was still and silent. The farmer was turning his team; the gulls were white behind the plough; the trees stood motionless, tipped with a warning yellow. When I left, one thing alone comforted me. That small place would remain unchanged in my lifetime. If ever I was able to return, the dream would never be broken by disenchantment.

CHAPTER ELEVEN

OF MIDNIGHT OIL

I APPROACHED London as probably did the pilots of German bombers. I felt excited, afraid, aware of its immensity, far from home, cold and tired. Some experience in the past, years in submarines perhaps, had told me that detailed cold-blooded planning was one part of success, and the other part depended on swift movement when opportunity arose. Death and glory had been frowned on in war. Applied to my particular problem, this meant that it was no good trying to write one vast epic, a best-seller with one eye on film rights. Something slower and more methodical was needed.

The plan on which I decided was to write on until one novel was accepted, await the views of the public and professional critics, and adjust things accordingly. Meanwhile, it would be necessary to find something to do which would bring in enough for basic necessities. This first plan turned out to be completely useless, for I discovered that the time between a book's acceptance and its publication was anything up to twelve months, and that if I waited for reviews before taking up my pen again, it would be years before anything was achieved.

The winter of 1946 was a particularly vicious one. Snow came down through naked branches and the wind was Siberian in origin. The old house in Chelsea in which I went to live was not able to withstand the weather and my bedroom became definitely wet. By day I worked in a room at the top of the house with a view over squat chimneys and an electric fire to keep my finger joints workable. That fire had character; it was made to look rather like a searchlight and threw off a beam of scorching heat in one small direction and for a short distance. If it was pointing away from me it was no use at all. If it was on the floor, cocked up to throw its heat my way, it singed the legs of my trousers. Sometimes I put it on the table beside me and as a result lost my eyelashes.

Luckily, I had been face to face with discomfort for a good many years, and neither the overall cold nor the local heat put a full stop to the work which I was doing. There were other difficulties. At that time I was trying to write about hot and sultry days in a street on the Cornish seaboard. Whenever I looked up from the paper I saw a black and yellow sky and snow-covered roof-tops and a bleakness of desolation. And then there were the synopses. They provided my bread and butter and were largely responsible for the piles of paper and carbon which were scattered about the room. Helped by introductions and a test, I had been listed as a reader by the European Story Department of an American film company. It all sounded too simple. All I had to do was to read the book, write a brief criticism, a summary in my own words and a synopsis, about ten pages, in the author's words as far as possible. There had to be six copies of the whole shooting match.

Sometimes, as I typed away, the snow mounting up on the outside of the windows and the fire glowing bleakly in the cold fog, I used to think that this was the funniest thing that had ever happened to me. How Irish Michael of the *Pommern* would have laughed, or Rambo, down by his crabber. Here I sat, trying to tell a distant American what I thought about books in which I had about as much interest as the publishers had in those I wrote myself. But it was not altogether amusing. I discovered that it was extremely difficult to condense a book into a matter of six thousand words without losing touch with the whole. Once condensed, it was not easy to assemble the copies in their right order, and quite often I found that one of the carbons was in the wrong way and that the only means Hollywood had of reading my work was to hold it up to a mirror.

While I turned out my synopses at a rate which supplied my needs and eventually brought about my downfall in the film world, the new novel progressed slowly, like a piece of knitting that is taken up at odd moments and somehow manages to reach an end. By this time, all the articles and short stories I had written in Cornwall had come back. The editors regretted with almost boring constancy. I even ceased becoming excited whenever the postman arrived.

Sitting in my ice-bound room I made a good many notes about writing for a living; some no doubt resulted from the fits of mental depression brought on by a particularly difficult synopsis. Others sprang from fits of triumphant glee when the six copies of twenty-two pages, 132 pages in all, were successfully driven into neat piles, gathered into a folder and put on one side. The only thing that prevented complete satisfaction at such a moment was that another book was always awaiting dehydration.

Rather shyly and feeling like an impostor, I began to take a look at the other men and women who were in the saddling enclosure on London's literary racecourse. There was one young man who was solemnly reading law at a university in order that he might earn enough as a solicitor to allow a leisurely writing of plays after office hours. His policy was long-term in the extreme. On the other hand, there were many more who sauntered from one literary agency to another with much pausing at stone-topped tables near Tottenham Court Road tube station to drink beer (Maupassant), and much night work with black coffee at their elbow (Balzac), and talk of their great epics (Tolstoy), and their religions (Dostoievsky). They all looked shabby and some wore red ties (D. H. Lawrence), while a few had slight American accents (Henry James).

I was, I fear, unable to enjoy their dreams, their hopes and disappointments. The sea is a great leveller; it brushes aside all pose, all the walls man builds up to conceal his inner weaknesses. So too life with the abrupt Cornish had made me look for some hard core within each stranger. Talk of ballet and the Third Programme and Sartre and Camus meant nothing. Behind it there was the same stark search for security and comfort, the same inner problems, the same wayward emotions that make up the short period between birth and death. What matter if one is an expert on Racine or on fertiliser? The human element is still the same.

I was in revolt against the impassioned love of all that was foreign, of all that was obscure. It seemed to me that the inspiration behind great Russian writings had been a crystal-clear vision of Russia, and the same applied to those of France or Germany or Spain. Clarity was to become one of my rules, and England was the backcloth. There was no shame in earning one's living by writing, for after all, no art of any value could survive in a vacuum of self-sufficiency. Judgment, with the other lasting truths, would have to await new generations. It is part of the nature of a classic that it cannot be recognised as such by contemporaries. This being the case, one great disappointment is ruled out. Authors cannot read their own obituaries.

One evening the telephone rang. I went downstairs, my eyes smarting with smoke and my head whirling with the outline of an awkward synopsis. I lifted the receiver and in fifteen seconds heard that my first novel had been accepted as it stood. I sat there for a long time and a brand-new world came into focus. I could hardly have been more pleased if I had been given the Nobel Peace Prize. On the strength of that news I decided to get married far sooner than I had thought possible, book seats to Paris, look for a house, scrap my last synopsis and have a large whisky in the pub round the corner. Caution was thrown to the winds. Had caution always been mankind's watchword, the human race would probably have become extinct or still be grubbing about for nuts in the forests of Central Africa.

But the publishers might have been alarmed had they known what their small advance was to achieve in elasticity.

*　　　*　　　*

We left the sun behind somewhere over the dry white grasses of the Rhône valley. The train crawled into the half-light of Victoria station. Our bags were full of wild flowers from the Mediterranean coast, a small sweet-smelling tribute to our room at the hotel, and unpacking was full of nostalgia. Tooth-glasses, soap-dishes, basins and bath were filled with iris, wild orchid, wallflower, anemone, and blossom. Outside, the grey clouds flew low over the roof-tops and it began to rain. Despite the flowers, reality broke through upon us.

We had approximately forty-eight hours in which to find a house, a minute bank balance, total employment, synopses and work in a literary agency on one hand, unclassified aid in art direction in film studios on the other. The house would therefore have to be somewhere between Denham and London. We worked out strategy and tactics, and made a grand assault on all estate agents along the Tube line from Piccadilly to Uxbridge. In one day we had a pleasant furnished house down in the beechwoods of Buckinghamshire. One thing at least was certain: we would be able to enjoy the long calm days of English summer.

It was a relief to get out of London. Long silent hours on the forecastle head of a becalmed barque, night watch on a submarine bridge off Sumatra, days in the cottage room by the Cornish coast, these had formed, for me at least, a foundation on which to build, a memory of the purest clearest hours when human life balanced on the knife-edge between the instinctive and the rational.

In the middle of July the proofs of my first two books arrived by the same post. With any luck they might be out before Christmas. I read them, lying out on the lawn under the evening sun and wondering whether they would bring pleasure to anybody. Any art is a means to an end, whether to make money, to achieve fame, to satisfy some latent instinct or to put over an idea. There is always a means and always an end. Whether the end be a literary perfection or a large bank account, pleasure for the reader is the aim. I remember the words of John Cowper Powys: "The poorest, the grossest, the shallowest, the most melodramatic of books carry with them *something*, some tincture, some essence, some suggestion, of the wisdom of the ages that has melted into this vast flood." The gulf between highbrow and lowbrow is about as wide as a hair of one's head; it is crossed by innumerable bridges; it is entirely artificial. How many of those who profess to enjoy Homer can read Greek? How many of those who despise serial writers proclaim a love for Dickens in the same breath? How many can one hear dismissing simplicity and story-telling, yet announcing that the Bible is great literature? The dust which falls so lightly on the unopened covers of many of to-day's clever obscure masterpieces will slowly thicken; it will conceal the book from the eyes of the next generation.

By the time we returned to London in the autumn, we both felt we were playing for the wrong teams. There were times when we looked at ourselves objectively and found the view was incredibly funny. I was tramping about London, trying to sell other people's work in order that I might work myself, sending three synopses a week to America while my books remained incomplete. The glamour of a film studio grows less and less as it is seen more clearly. It is like an exotic fruit, the best side turned upward. Beneath the glare of lights it shrivels and dries until the lower half is revealed.

We went to parties. "Do you," I was asked, "actually have to talk to authors? How awful. They're quite impossible of course." "Having lunch is such a waste of time, so bourgeois." "I have written a little thing, just a pleasant piece about the love of a homicidal maniac for his dog. Would you care to read it? I had thought of the films. I suppose you don't know anyone . . ." "I haven't been in the right mood for the last week." ". . . quite spoilt by love interest, you know . . ."

One day in autumn we were leaning over Chelsea Bridge, idly watching some men working on old boats that lay down on the shining mud. My eyes were half-closed against a golden sunlight. I could almost imagine that I was in Cornwall, looking down at the inner side of the beach. Perhaps if I turned my head I would see the green cliffs and the blue bay and the ships on the horizon. Perhaps . . . Out of that vision there came a sudden suggestion and then a decisive plan. We would take the next train out of it all, down to the stark village between the cornfields and the sea. Caution was forgotten. It would not be a journey to any bemused ivory tower, or to a sheltered sunlit glade, but one to the hard black and white of

the walls, to the searing sincerity, to the edge of a granite cliff where
the winter was throbbing in from the west and the gales howling
over the flat land. It would be a return to what was indestructible
England. Some said we were going to a backwater where nothing
ever happened. They were quite wrong.

We arrived at Vine Cottage on one of those autumn evenings
when the sea lay like dull metal between the cliffs, and the clouds
were thin and high, the air still, the smoke like a blue mist over the
valley, the sun shining in pale patches over the fields and water. A
fire flickered in the little room and all the windows were wide open
to the soft whisper of the waves. That was the beginning of the
journey; the end of one short span in our lives.

There was in the decision to return there an acceptance of
normality, a realisation perhaps that no new idea of value could be
quickly perceived through the smoke of a post-war city. A move
to the west was an escape, but it was an escape to reality. Down
there it was possible to watch the battle between the ideal and the
purely necessary being fought on simple lines. Whoever won, it
seemed that the country would be gripped by the law of compulsion.
The press-gang has never been the best of institutions, and those who
volunteered for service in submarines and were up against sweat and
discomfort and great monotony were told: "You have the choice.
Like it or get out." And then pride came to the rescue.

We were down on the edge of the sea by choice, facing the force
of the Atlantic gales, walking down to the tap for our drinking
water, accepting certain hardships in return for certain freedoms.
And before us the cycle of the year moved slowly.

There was a still grey evening when we walked back over the
headland, over the fog-shrouded fields, a kitten tucked away in the
warmth of a coat, while the fog-horn on the Lizard boomed out and
the ships answered in querulous bleats from the hidden sea. It was
Guy Fawkes night. The bonfires sent a diffused glow from the beach,
the rockets becoming lost in the upper darkness. The fishermen
had caught some pilchards and were gathered around a hurricane
lamp, the nets spread out and the fish shining like sudden stars of

blue light. January arrived, bringing with it our only light fall of snow and the first sight of the daffodil shoots. Winter became spring in one breathless morning. There were perfect days, pale and still with the sun rising into a clear sky and the sea green and quiet except where the tide moved along the rocks. The gorse bushes were patterned silver with spiders' webs. Red campion grew in the hedges, and the ploughed fields were rich and dark between the green fringes. Sometimes it was difficult to believe that it was winter. The pines were black against an indigo sky; the village walls gleamed white as they absorbed the sunlight. Only at night did the cold return. Even then the night sky was full of stars and the sea gleamed in its passivity.

In March the first boats appeared on the beach and the new pots were stacked above the tide. Jinnah the kitten seemed to sense that fish would soon appear on his menu and became frisky and alert. In the same week we found over a hundred different wild flowers along the cliff path to the east. The flow of the year increased in momentum. Within, we worked hard, going out in the lengthening evenings or when the French crabbers came in to anchor, or when the lifeboat went out to the call of a green rocket that shattered the silence. Summer came with a light washing of blue air against the rocks and the shimmer of the sea blinding us when we looked out in the early morning. Summer was a time of light and shadow, of boats lying out on the translucent water, of dead calm nights when the only sound was the song of the men as they left the pub. The stars were very clear and white beyond the cool smokeless atmosphere.

And so the hot days dawdled into short ones and the winds returned and our first year drew to a close. For me it was the first time I had spent any one year in one place and had seen the whole cycle of nature swing before me. It had been a year of sowing and blooming and dying, harvest and spawning and fruit. I had sensed the mystic of the soil and the legend of the sea. I loved the life there, and grew to appreciate the necessity of careful balance between thought and action, criticism and experience, intellect and instinct.

I believe now that I have found a place in which to live where my thoughts are free, where no screens of artificiality, snobbery or sickness hide the simple truths on which are based those greater springs of knowledge towards which we all reach. This village, old-fashioned, secluded, away from the main stream, has survived for four hundred years, through wars and revolutions, through changes of religious and political thought, through the birth and death of kings, statesmen, artists and ideas. The cities adopt, as they rightly should, each new doctrine; they swing and turn on a word from an orator, on a page from a writer; they fluctuate and die. Behind them they know that they have a solid England, an England of villages such as this, unchanging, unalterable, the bone and muscle of a great land. If this place, and others like it, were to lose their ability to stand firm, then the bones would soften and the body become flabby and the country's death merely depend on the passing of time.

Before us, as this second year begins, we have pen and brush and a pile of white and empty paper. The words and pictures with which we cover the pages must be drawn from a combination of imagination and experience; they must therefore have their origin in both thought and action. If either spring dies the result will be dusty fantasy or crude realism. In this stark setting we hope to find a compromise.

Now, outside the window, a young moon shines over the sea; the tide is low; the wind has died away. The lighthouse sends its beam out over the dark water, out from the cliffs, out over the rocks, out past moving ships, out to the dark line of the clear-cut horizon. To the horizon shines the light, and from the horizon comes the gleaming track of a starpath. Beyond that point we are unable to see.

MEMORY BAY

In December the rain came in from the Atlantic in a grey wall; it flattened the white sea, pattered on the granite cliffs and then poured on the land. The trees leaned away towards the east; the flowers bent; the little paths became streams and the fields were shining silver where the water lay. After the quiet rain, the wind came as well, and the gales pounded the sea into streaks of white which showed faintly through the thickness of falling drops.

In December I returned to Caerleon. It was simple enough to walk up along the cliff path when a gap in the clouds showed bright blue and the sea was patched and vivid. Between us swung the canvas grip, and Jinnah's nose protruded from a tiny opening in the zip fastener, searching for fresh smells and eager to be out. We crossed the broken-down walls and passed under the shelter of the pine tree. The old gate swung open on rusted hinges; the path was barely discernible; the grass was thick where once flowers had grown.

Much was the same there, but much had changed. The cottage had been empty for a while, and it seemed to welcome us as if it was lonely on the wild stretch of heath with nothing in sight but the wide bay and nothing to hear but the occasional windblown note of the school bell. We stood within the skyline of field and the horizon of water. There was in the drenched and sodden garden, overgrown with years of neglect during the war, a sense of black desolation. But then, in the same moment, we saw the violets struggling in the grass and the tips of daffodil shoots appearing in the wet earth. Our imaginations sped to the summer to come, and we turned towards the door.

The wind poured over the roof and rain rattled against the windows. The cottage seemed lifeless, but minute by minute life began to return. Water flowed in the pipes like blood, throbbing from room to room, warming, beating within the steel arteries. The fire flickered in the sitting-room, and the lights glowed softly on the beams. Jinnah began a tour of exploration, discovering a family of mice under the stairs with which he soon forgot the fears of an unknown home. The old well to which we had once carried buckets each morning was rusty and forgotten, for an electric pump now hummed away behind the tank, and there was no need to go down through the wild night.

There perhaps was the end of one cycle of hope. The span of twenty years between the sowing of a dream's seed and the realisation was governed largely by chance. Fate often blows as a contrary wind, and one is forced to sail obliquely from the planned destination. Free will does not permit a man to change the wind's direction, but he can go about on the other tack and sail close to the wind, and that may be his salvation.

Within Caerleon, twenty years dwindle to a mere moment of time. The cottage has stood upon this cliff top for over four centuries. The past leaps up and haunts. Each time we glance at the beam over the open fireplace, we know it to be part of a ship's keel, hurled, in some long-forgotten storm, upon the beach below. And the jib-boom which holds up part of the bedroom ceiling must have cast its thin shadow on many sunlit quays. We wonder who carved the shape of the old keel. Was it a shipwright from Cumberland or Essex? Was it a settler in New England, or a Russian or a Spaniard? Who was it who laboured to build the outer walls of huge blocks of granite and planted the pine tree beyond the garden?

Those are the only ghosts, small and insignificant signs of long-past work. The cottage, the hard tracks, the broad stone walls around the fields, the gaps in the cliff from which granite was once quarried, these things are still here. Born in sweat and toil, they stand fast, and the generation whose hands scarred the rocks and topsoil leave a great memorial to inspire their weaker successors.

This is a quiet place, peaceful in the extreme. It is a land into which a man may sink his roots deep. Those who have been brought up in its tradition are a part of the granite, some hard and unrelenting as they plough the wide fields within sight of the old Methodist chapel, some easy-going and pagan in the sunlight where the nets are hung to dry. In the long still hours between the storms they are out under the sky, moving slowly and quietly, but with firm step, around their allotted tasks.

The sword and the marlinspike have been discarded. In their place are the garden spade and the pen. All is peaceful under a calm sky, and the only enemies are the wild garlic and nettles and slugs. But it is in the still places, far from the clamour of conference, that one first hears the pride and strength of a country stirring. Here, the enemy who seeks to disrupt must take guard, for as he shouts his pointless way through the cities a slight sound might be heard in the still evening by the bay. Through that clear air comes the click of a sword that is half-drawn.

There are deep shadows across the bay, a rich blueness that is an even backcloth to the shimmer of daffodils as they dance in the sea breeze. The blackthorn is like new snow along the hedges and the gorse gleams with a fierce light. The green of the spring is rising like coloured smoke between the walls. It is the dawn of a new year.